NATURE WATCH

NATURE WATCH

Julian Pettifer and Robin Brown

With the assistance of Malcolm Whitehead

HarperCollins*Publishers*

HarperCollins*Publishers*
London • Glasgow • Sydney
Auckland • Toronto • Johannesburg

This publication is based on the television series *Nature Watch*
produced by Central Independent Television plc

CENTRAL

First published 1994

ISBN 000 219 956 4

Printed and bound by Butler & Tanner Ltd,
Frome, Somerset

CONTENTS

FOREWORD

It is more than ten years since we met at a New Year's Eve party and discussed the possibility of finding a *different* way of presenting natural history on television. At that time, programme style was very much technology-led. The rapid development of new cameras, lenses and filming techniques meant that TV producers could always expect to amaze and enchant their audiences with new revelations about animal behaviour. There was always a new 'gee whiz' factor: marvels guaranteed to hold the viewing public spellbound.

Both of us, while admiring what the new technology could provide and the artistry of these film-makers, felt that it was beginning to dominate old-fashioned story telling and 'human interest'. It may be that we reached that conclusion because we came to natural history obliquely. Robin was a news producer, documentary film maker and novelist who one day became hooked on dolphins and made them the subject of several films and a much acclaimed book *The Lure of the Dolphin*. Julian was a current affairs reporter who in the course of his day to day work found himself covering some of the environmental horror stories that started to emerge during the sixties and seventies. Both of us felt that natural history, as presented in the cinema or on television, usually fell into two predictable categories: the arch and cutesy Never-Never Land of furry animals pioneered by Disney, or a beautifully photographed Garden of Eden where Adam and Eve never intruded and where creatures pursued their private lives totally untroubled by man.

It occurred to us that the kind of natural history television that worked best for us (and millions of others) were the programmes where the natural world was interpreted by an engaging expert; hence the great success enjoyed by Davids Attenborough and Bellamy. But why not extend that happy formula and let some of the legion of enthusiasts and experts around the world convey to a wider audience their particular passion for the natural world? That was the question that was put to the management of ATV and very quickly they saw the point. The result was the launch of *Nature Watch*, a series of television programmes that allowed zoologists and botanists, artists and photographers, ecologists and ordinary men and women to present their enthusiasms and concerns and fears and joys about wildlife to a wider audience.

Once we had been given the go-ahead by ATV our most pressing task was to select the subjects for our first thirteen films. The earliest lesson we learned was the most important: that the crucial question was not *what* interested our Naturewatchers but *how* they conveyed their interest and passion. In conventional natural history films, there is a bias towards large, exotic animals because it is assumed that people dislike small, slimy or scaly ones. We proved that if you have someone like Australian photographer and writer Densey Clyne as your guide, you can find marvels in every suburban back garden.

Julian Pettifer filming Nature Watch *with a baby elephant in Kenya*

Seen through he eyes of the right naturalist, one like Densey, a starling can be as fascinating as the rarest parrot, the hunting strategy of a spider more intriguing than that of a lioness and a newt as interesting as a crocodile. Densey has an enthusiasm for invertebrate animals: for the insects and spiders, slugs and snails, caterpillars and their kind which most of us fail to observe and which when we do spot them are more likely to attack with a shudder or an insect spray than to drop on our knees to admire. Densey was able to convey her own sense of wonder at the activities in the 'garden jungle' surrounding her home in Sydney and, judging from our mail bag, she awakened a similar response in many of our viewers.

In that first series we even included a programme on Dr. Miriam Rothschild who is probably the world's leading authority on bird fleas – not, you would think, the most promising subject for a popular, prime-time TV series – but the public tuned in by their millions. For many years *Nature Watch* was the highest rating factual television series of any kind on ITV. The reason is very simple: most people relate to other people more easily than they relate to elephants or woodlice; but you can interest them in woodlice and elephants if you have the right intermediary. Our task was to find those very special intermediaries. In the end, we became quite good at it; but we did make one spectacular mistake. We selected a Naturewatcher who was eminent in her field, articulate and personable. She was the very first subject we ever filmed, but after two days our production team was in despair. At first we could not work out what was going wrong, and why the story was failing to come alive. It was Robin who put his finger on the trouble: "She's too much of an egoist", he said, "more interested in presenting herself than the animals". He was right. Since then we have featured plenty of Naturewatchers with strong personalities and well-developed egos but in every case it is the subject of their passion that they want to project and not themselves. Moreover, that judgment of the core theme of *Nature Watch* was quickly vindicated by our next outing with arguably the most famous natural scientist to appear in the series, Nobel Prize-winning laureate, Professor Konrad Lorenz. Konrad was not short of ego, indeed he had a huge, exuberant personality, but when asked to summarise his vast range of interests he laughed and replied: "That is quite simple. I am a watcher of nature. It is my obsession."

Carl Jones (Chapter 5) is an irreverent, irrepressible Welshman and certainly not reticent about his work in Mauritius; but what he has done for that island's wildlife is truly remarkable. He has saved two birds from certain extinction, set another on the road to possible recovery and helped change an entire society's attitude towards conservation. Yet what came across in the two *Nature Watch* programmes we made with Carl was not in any way self-congratulatory. On the contrary, he made it clear that his small victories only serve to signpost one way forward in the seemingly overwhelming task of saving endangered species.

It is no coincidence that Carl Jones is a close friend of Don Merton. As one series of *Nature Watch* followed another, we found that the best way to find new subjects was to consult those we had already featured in earlier series. Fortunately most, if not all of them, had enjoyed the filming experience and understood very well what we were looking for. They responded with numerous suggestions and very rarely set us on the wrong track.

Thinking back over the *Nature Watch* years, we have been trying to work out why it was such a very happy experience. It was partly because the production team – film crews, directors and researchers – were such congenial people; *and* we journeyed to some of the most beautiful and remote parts of the planet; *and* we filmed some of its most spectacular wildlife; but, above all, we had the company of those Naturewatchers who enjoyed so much sharing their knowledge of the natural world and their delight in it. We shall never forget walking out with Erik Zimen and his wolves in flower-strewn Alpine meadows; or resting with Mark Stanley-Price and his Bedouin friends under the brilliant desert stars in the Empty Quarter; or wading waist-deep with Ken Livingstone, paralytic with laughter, as we searched for newts in a disused swimming pool; or wandering with Mike Donoghue through a derelict whaling station in New Zealand and pondering its grim history; or that crazy day with Carl Jones when a large fruit bat escaped his grasp and began to crawl up Julian's bare leg leaving a bloody trail of claw marks. "Don't move" yelled Carl as the creature was about to disappear up the leg of his shorts. For once, Julian ignored the advice of the expert and blocked the bat's advances. "You had nothing to worry about", Carl assured him as he recaptured the animal. "They don't eat nuts".

The one thing you will never suffer in the company of Naturewatchers is boredom. They enjoy our world and they are doing what they can to understand and to protect it. No task on earth is more important than that and we have been privileged to join them.

In bringing this book to press, we acknowledge the help we received with the text from Malcolm Whitehead; and for the picture research our thanks go to Bryony Kinnear for her diligence and impeccable judgement.

Julian Pettifer and Robin Brown, June 1993

CHAPTER ONE
CHIMPANZEE CRUSADE

Chimpanzees are our closest living relatives. Biochemically we share ninety-nine per cent of the same DNA sequences with these complex, noisy, excitable African apes. This means that, in evolutionary terms, we are nearer to chimps than chimps are to monkeys or horses are to donkeys. Some scientists even suggest that people should be reclassified as another living chimpanzee species.

Yet if the chimpanzee is our biological brother, we are guilty of fratricide on a grand scale. Habitat destruction, hunting and poaching for biomedical research and beach photography have pushed the chimpanzee to the very edge of extinction in the wild.

Naturewatcher Jane Goodall scanning the Tanzanian hillside for chimpanzees

Someone who knows more about chimpanzees than anyone else is Naturewatcher Dr Jane Goodall. She has made chimp welfare her personal crusade, both in the wild and in captivity. Her zeal was born and nourished in Tanzania, where, at the Gombe Stream Reserve, a lifetime of research has brought her a unique understanding of our closest cousin. Jane's thirty year study, the longest on any animal in the wild, has convinced her that chimps deserve our special consideration.

Jane Goodall spent her childhood in Bournemouth on England's south coast, and in London. She was always interested in animals and made copious notes about the birds she saw around her home. After several trips to London Zoo, she vowed that one day she would visit Africa and see the same species living free. Accordingly, after leaving school, she took some secretarial courses and presented herself at the Coryndon Museum in Nairobi, Kenya.

It was there she met Louis Leakey, a self taught Kenyan anthropologist who went on to receive degrees from Cambridge University and worldwide fame for his fossil hominid discoveries at Olduvai Gorge, a remote site on Tanzania's Serengeti Plain. During one visit to the Gorge, Leakey told Jane, by then his assistant secretary, about the wild chimpanzees that strayed from the forests and congregated on the shores of Lake Tanganyika. The apes fled if humans appeared. But supposing someone could win their trust and follow their daily lives. Nobody had done that before. A young student, sent by Leakey years earlier, had given up after six months. Maybe someone could habituate the chimpanzees to the presence of people. It would take a person of great dedication and patience. Maybe that someone was Jane Goodall.

Three years later, in 1960, Jane first surveyed the shores of Lake Tanganyika. The interim period had been spent learning about primates at the Royal Free Hospital and London Zoo while Leakey sought funds. Civil war had recently raged through East Africa and, much to Jane's frustration, Tanzania's post colonial government was not about to allow a lone English woman into the bush. However, they relented when Jane's mother, Vanne, arrived at the base camp.

Gombe Stream Reserve is a magical place. The beach is six hundred metres above sea level and from it rise hills carpeted with rich tropical gallery forest. Some of the

Jane Goodall with a chimp in Gombe Stream Reserve. It took her over a year to habituate the chimps to her presence

trees reach twenty five metres in height. Outside the forest, open woodland covers the upper slopes and tall grasses protrude from the peaks and ridges.

Jane set out to look for chimps. Her African guides taught her how to travel through the forest along trails made by baboons and bushpigs. They showed her the msulula trees with their red and orange fruits, a particular chimpanzee favourite. Jane saw her first wild chimps in a msulula tree — a group of sixteen who stayed feeding in and around the tree for ten days.

Then two months elapsed. No more chimps were seen, the funds were almost spent, and Jane succumbed to a tropical fever. Aware of the difficulties of finding apes, let alone habituating them, Jane persevered and, one day, saw three chimps eighty metres away through her binoculars. Soon others joined the trio. Amazingly, they ignored Jane. Her slow, deliberate movements did not threaten them.

It took over a year to habituate the Gombe chimpanzees. Jane followed a rigorous daily routine. She rose at 5.30am, breakfasted on bread and coffee, packed her

David Greybeard and some of the other members of the group of chimps first studied by Jane Goodall

thermos flask and always wore the same fawn-coloured shirts, shorts and tennis shoes so as not to surprise or upset the chimps. Then she tied her blonde hair into a pony tail and trekked from dawn to dusk , writing everything down as it happened.

Soon Jane began to recognise individual chimpanzees, and gave them names. There was Flo, an adult female with a distinctive ugly bulbous nose; Mr McGregor, named after a farmer in a Beatrix Potter story; Goliath, a huge male, and David Greybeard. "Every chimpanzee is as different from another as we humans are," says

Jane. "They all have their unique personalities and even now after thirty years in the field we're still learning completely new things about them."

Some of Jane's early discoveries rocked the international scientific community. David Greybeard was always one of the more forward chimps - it was he who first let Jane approach within ten metres. One day, Jane watched David fashion a blade of grass, stick it into a termite nest and fish out the succulent insect meals. These were revolutionary observations. At the time, the accepted definition of the human species was that we are the only animal to use tools. Jane hastily telegrammed Leakey and the implications of the finding triggered a hot scientific debate. Should the definition of man be amended, or should the chimpanzee be classified alongside the human?

"We now know that tool using is something that's learned," says Jane Goodall. "The child watches its mother, brothers and sisters, and other individuals in the group." Thanks to Jane's research it was proved beyond doubt that chimps teach their offspring to make and use tools. "And this is why you can look back and think that

Chimpanzees will use a blade of grass or little twig to 'fish' for termites to eat

each tool-using pattern that you see in any chimp group was obviously the invention of some chimpanzee genius in the far distant past."

As more researchers studied chimps in different parts of Africa, it was found that tool-use varies from area to area. West African chimpanzees at one site employ a hammer and anvil technique to open hard shell fruits with flat stones and thick pieces of wood. At Gombe the most frequently seen tool is a blade of grass or a little twig for fishing for termites and white ants. Sometimes the chimps crumple leaves into a kind of sponge to sop water from hollows in tree trunks that they cannot reach with their lips. They use long sticks to fish for very vicious biting ants, sweeping the stick through the hand and gnashing the ants with the teeth. Occasionally they hurl rocks or brandish sticks as weapons.

It was David Greybeard who Jane first saw eating meat. At the time, chimps were thought to be vegetarian, feasting on ripe fruits, leaves, flowers, pith, resins and bark. Such plant products do make up the bulk of their diet, but, as well as insects, larger animals like monkeys and antelope are sometimes taken.

One winter's morning, Jane noticed an excited group of chimps clustered around David who was tearing away at a wrinkly pink object with his teeth. Nearby stood a female bush pig – David Greybeard was eating her baby.

Although fruit, leaves, flowers and other plant products make up the bulk of a chimpanzee's diet, they also eat insects and hunt for meat - monkey or even antelope.

Today we know that hunting is a regular feature of chimp society. Normally it is the province of a few older, experienced males. Recently a BBC Natural History Unit team filmed a chimpanzee hunt in the Ivory Coast's Tai National Park. Millions of viewers were alternately enthralled and sickened as the chimps adopted a well rehearsed hunting strategy to catch an adult colobus monkey and rip it apart still alive. Each hunter knew its job. There were beaters, ambushers, chasers and the killer.

Given the great variability between chimp populations, it is not surprising that the Gombe animals hunt in different ways from their western counterparts. There is less cooperation during the hunt and more aggression involved in food sharing afterwards. Tai chimps prefer adult colobus monkeys. Gombe chimps seek out the infants, often releasing the mother unharmed. In Gombe, but not in the Tai, adult male colobus harass chimp hunters, frequently causing them to retreat or drop their quarry.

In 1965, Jane founded the Gombe Stream Research Centre. By now, she had studied animal behaviour at Leakey's alma mater, Cambridge University, who awarded her a PhD. People were beginning to hear about the serene English woman who lived with apes, and soon volunteers began arriving at Gombe to help with the work. Some were inexperienced enthusiasts; later helpers were student biologists and qualified field workers. The National Geographical Society started to underwrite the project and provided funds for a series of permanent buildings at the base camp.

This was much needed. Eighteen months after the chimp project started, David Greybeard and Goliath turned the tables and decided to observe Jane in her home environment. The two males quickly realised that the ramshackle camp provided numerous opportunities for stealing bananas, and after word got out, a dozen or so chimps were regularly coming to visit. The camp was wrecked as the same animals that Jane could not approach within one hundred metres two years earlier, discovered the delights of chewing tents and sucking T-shirts to obtain the salty sweat.

The solution seemed to be to construct a feeding station, but that too got out of hand. Upwards of fifty chimps were coming to eat at Jane's lakeside diner, and they were joined by hordes of hungry baboons. The situation could best be described as open warfare, and it was caused by human interference.

Finally, a compromise was reached. Jane reworked feeding devices so that individual chimps could be fed irregularly when she chose. There followed an uneasy truce. Then, unexpectedly, the fifty chimps split into two distinct groups, a northern group (the Kasakela community) and a southern group (the Kahama community).

Chimpanzees live in loose communities of fifteen to over one hundred animals, but the entire group is rarely together. Small parties split off and forage independently. Such liaisons may consist of any combinations of males, females and young. Males and females normally seek the company of their own sex unless females are in season. It appears that males seldom leave their birth group although females may transfer to neighbouring groups during adolescence. The entire group inhabits a territory that may be defended by male 'border patrols' who chase outsiders away.

It is in observing and understanding the group structure where the long term nature of Jane Goodall's research came into its own. Understanding chimps takes time - not months, not even years. A fuller picture is only revealed with decades of patient study. During the early 1970's a previously undescribed pattern of chimpanzee behaviour began to emerge at Gombe. The northern Kasakela community began an aggressive expansionist policy and groups of marauding males systematically picked off individuals from the southern Kahama community and killed them. Over a period of seven years, the smaller splinter group was completely destroyed as the invading northern hordes gradually extended their range southwards. The colonists enjoyed their expanded environment for about a year before another group who lived even further south (the Kalande community) started challenging them. Gradually the Kasakela chimps were pushed back to the north until they occupied a territory smaller than their pre-expansionist space.

This can only be described as warfare, something else once thought unique to our own species. As Jane Goodall says,"at Gombe we have probably seen behaviours similar to those in our own ancestors that eventually led to human warfare."

"I have a high level of emotional involvement with many of the Gombe chimps," says Jane Goodall. "One of the most fascinating aspects of the work is the long term pictures you get of family histories. There are long lasting bonds between mothers and their youngsters, particularly between brothers and sisters, and between other members of the community. For me, it's always been the most appealing to watch the relationship develop between a mother and her offspring over the years. The development of the infant chimpanzee follows so many of the same patterns and stages as the human child. And the relationship between the mother and her older offspring is especially interesting. The child doesn't even begin to start leaving the mother until it is eight or nine years old. Then it is only away for a short time before coming back to travel around again with mum and the younger brothers and sisters."

The study of Flo's family spanned twenty-six research years and is central to Jane Goodall's understanding of chimpanzee relationships. Thereafter, Jane confined her activities to observation, and steadily built a picture of chimpanzee society based around Flo, her sons (Fagen, Figen, Flame and Flint) and daughter (Fifi). One son,

The development of young chimpanzees follows many of the same patterns and stages as a human child

Flint, was particularly special. He was the first chimpanzee whose development was chronicled from birth by Jane.

When Flo grew old and died, she was probably around fifty years of age. Flint stayed by the body for one day then fell into a state of deep depression. He died three and a half weeks later. Fifi went on to have two sons (Freud and Frodo) and two daughters (Fanni and Flossi). She too grieved after her mother's death and spent most of the time away from the group. Flo became the only chimpanzee to merit an obituary in the Sunday Times. "Flo has contributed much to science," it read. "It is true that her life enriched human understanding. But even if no one had studied the chimpanzees at Gombe, Flo's life, rich and full of vigour and love, would still have had a meaning and a significance in the pattern of things."

Sometimes when a chimpanzee mother dies, the baby is adopted by its older brother or sister. The first orphan that Jane saw at Gombe was a four to five year old male called Merlin. Merlin's mother, Marina, died and he went into a state of depression manifested by plucking great clumps of hair from his legs and arms. After a while, Merlin's thighs were completely bare, and the youngster had become so lethargic that he did not have the energy of will to get out of the way of charging males. He was eventually adopted by his sister Miff who was eight to nine years old at the time. Merlin never really recovered from his mother's death, however, and became progressively emaciated. Eighteen months later, in his weak condition he succumbed to the polio epidemic that spread through the Gombe chimp population in the mid 1960s.

The most sinister filial relationship that developed at Gombe was between a female called Passion and her daughter Pom. Passion treated Pom very harshly but the two formed a psychotic duo who went around killing and eating the babies of other females over a four year period in the 1970s. Jane saw this happen on three occasions, but suspects that Passion and Pom may have committed infanticide and cannibalism on another seven missing chimp babies. Because of scientific objectivity, Jane was powerless to intervene. Her emotional involvement with the animals made this a very worrying period. "I think I hated Passion at the time," says Jane. Her opinion was amended in 1982 when Passion suffered severe abdominal pains and died from an unusual wasting disease. "How could I go on hating her?" she says. "She was not a human - she could scarcely be held responsible for her behaviour."

If cannibalism and warfare demonstrated the darker side of chimp nature, there were daily observations at Gombe that testified to the great cognitive abilities, problem solving skills and depths of kinship bonding in the African apes. A lot of these were learnt as infants played.

"There are two kinds of play," says Jane Goodall. "You have play when the chimp is alone which is acrobatic and involves turning somersaults, twirling around in trees or playing with objects.

"Then of course there's social play. This can be gentle, particularly if a small infant is one of the play partners. Or it can be very wild and involve four or five youngsters chasing around through the trees. It sometimes ends in squabbles and fighting but not for very long."

Young chimpanzees playing. Play is important for the development of physical skills and for learning the rules and regulations of chimp society

Jane believes that play is important in helping the infant to hone its physical skills and learn about the complicated rules and regulations of chimp society.

No one knows how many chimpanzees live wild in Africa. Up to 200,000 may exist in a variety of suitable forest habitats, but the best current (albeit speculative) population estimates are between 40,000 and 100,000. Of the twenty African nations that harbour wild chimp populations, only Gabon and Zaire contain large numbers (65,000 and potentially 80,000 respectively). Other groups are scattered in small isolated pockets throughout the remainder of the species' range.

The main threats to chimpanzees are from hunting, poaching for human research and habitat loss. In some areas, hunting for 'bushmeat' is prevalent as the main source of dietary protein. Chimps are large, easily noticed targets.

Because they are so like us and can mimic our ways, chimps are frequently exploited for entertainment and regularly appear in TV adverts for tea and films (remember Tarzan's Cheetah or the chimp that starred with Ronald Reagan in a forgettable 'B' movie?). Although it may seem innocent and harmless, Jane Goodall believes that it is difficult – if not impossible – to train chimps to take part in stunts without some degree of coercion.

Chimpanzees have long been used for biomedical and other research. The famous first stop into space was taken not by man but for man by a terrified chimpanzee. Ham was the first ape to orbit Planet Earth as part of the US Space Programme. He did this in 1961, and press photographs show the return of the smiling simian. Anyone who knows chimpanzees will recognise the classic fear grin.

Students of language have also used chimpanzees as research tools. Washoe was the first chimp to learn American deaf and dumb sign language. Over four years she amassed a vocabulary of one hundred and thirty signs. Since then other apes have performed as well or better. Sign language research is controversial. While some claim that chimps are imitating the actions of researchers, the evidence to suggest that they understand what they are 'saying' (signing) is almost overwhelming.

Biomedical research, principally into the diseases of AIDS and hepatitis B (which chimps can be infected with but remain well), is carried out on chimpanzees. There are vast ethical, conservation and welfare problems involved. First, is it moral to test the effects of human drugs and diseases on chimpanzees? If we do not (and will not) use human guinea pigs, what right have we to subject our closest cousin to such research? Even on a physiological level, chimpanzees and people do not display identical reactions to certain medical conditions and 'cures'. Second, where do the chimpanzees used in such research come from? Trade in wild caught chimps is illegal under international wildlife laws, but it persists to Japan, Europe and the USA. Third, chimps in laboratories often endure appalling conditions.

Jane Goodall is mortified by the treatment of chimpanzees at human hands. After visiting one research institution she remarked, "that was a day that will haunt me for the rest of my life. It's one thing to see chimpanzees insane on film, and it is quite another to see it with your own eyes, to look at a young chimp, a three year old, who stares out with that blank look that you sometimes see on a child who has lost a mother or father. A chimp who should be full of life sitting listless, being lifted out by a keeper, sitting like a rag doll, being put back inside... and the size of the cages. Two three year old chimps in cages measuring fifty-five centimetres square and sixty centimetres high. They had already been in there for five months at least when I saw them."

Experiences like that motivated Jane to form her own society for chimpanzees - The Jane Goodall Institute*. The organisation supports research that helps chimps; both by forming the scientific baseline for conservation measures to protect them in the wild, and by devising ways of enriching the environment of captive animals. It also aims to spread the news about chimpanzee biology and exploitation to as wide a public as possible.

One heinous activity that Jane Goodall is trying to stop is the export of live wild-caught infant chimpanzees to unscrupulous photographers in Spain and the Canary Islands. The babies are carried around popular tourist haunts like beaches and nightclubs. Their owners entice holiday-makers to have snapshots taken with the unfortunate apes. It is believed that for every ten baby chimps captured from the wild, ten mothers are killed, twenty adult males are killed defending their families, and six out of every ten babies captured may die in transit.

A growing trend is to kill nursing mothers for bushmeat *and* take the baby for export. It is not uncommon to see baby chimpanzees with gaping wounds, shotgun pellets and other evidence of the hunters' presence.

Spanish beach chimps often develop abnormal behaviour patterns following a life

* The Jane Goodall Institute, 15 Clarendon Park, Lymington, Hants SO41 8AX

A beach photographer with a young chimp. It is believed that for every ten baby chimps captured from the wild, ten mothers and 20 adult males are killed defending their families. Six out of every ten captured die in transit

in impoverished isolation. They are frequently drugged with tranquillisers or marijuana to keep them docile. Many have their teeth pulled out, often with pliers, to prevent biting. Sometimes they are beaten up or burnt with cigarettes to render them submissive. A large number contract diseases from people, and once too old and dangerous to work, are normally killed or sold for biomedical research.

The racket is apparently very profitable. A photographer can take over one hundred photos a day at between ten and twenty dollars a photo. The importation of wild caught chimps into Spain is illegal but enforcement of the law by the authorities has been very patchy.

Nature Watch filmed Jane Goodall helping to rescue two Spanish beach chimps called Charlie and Butch. The chimps had been taken from the photographers and sent to the home of Simon and Peggy Templer.

"If you look at the overall picture, you just feel helpless," says Jane. "But if you take a piece of the picture, then I think you can do a lot. A perfect example is Simon and Peggy Templer who first took a chimp away from the Spanish beaches in the early 1970s. She was a young female called Jenny, who like Charlie and Butch, had been severely abused."

Since then, in the wooded hills of Catalonia, the Templers have turned their home into a refugee centre. Over the years they have cared for forty battered, ill-treated but rescued chimps.

Simon Templer thinks that the chimps are smuggled into the Canary Islands on small tramp steamers. From there they are farmed out and sold to the photographers. Once on the Canaries – and hence on Spanish territory – they can be flown internally anywhere in Spain. Apparently chimps have also turned up on the beaches of Israel and Mexico.

The Templer Sanctuary is a half-way house. They cannot keep the animals indefinitely so Charlie and Butch were about to be translocated to a permanent sanctuary in Dorset, England.

Jane instantly saw that both chimps had been through hell. Charlie had had all his teeth knocked out with a hammer. Fortunately the second set were now coming through. Simon explained that one chimp he had looked after had thirty cigarette burns on its face and arms. "We even had one who was a drug addict," he said. "It took six months for her to recover. Every afternoon at exactly the same time she would retreat to a corner of the cage and bang her head on the floor. It was the time when her previous owner injected her."

When the translocation operation began, both chimps were sedated - a necessary step in order to carry out a thorough veterinary inspection. Jane thought that Charlie had been on drugs because he tried to inject himself with the needle and, when that proved impossible, offered his arm to Jane for injection.

Both chimps were carefully placed in crates and loaded onto a truck for the first part of the journey to Dorset. Thanks to unyielding bureaucracy at both ends, a trip

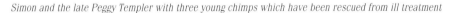

Simon and the late Peggy Templer with three young chimps which have been rescued from ill treatment

Naturewatcher Jim Cronin with a rescued chimp at Monkey World in Dorset

that should have taken twenty-four hours took forty-eight. Every one was exhausted.

The next day, Butch and Charlie's spirits were undampened as they welcomed a fresh start in a new country. Monkey World lies in deepest Dorset between the towns of Bere Regis and Wool. It was established by Steve Matthews and Jim Cronin, an expert on captive primate husbandry and former keeper at several major English and American zoological collections. Both men are committed to primate conservation and keep their animals in as near natural conditions as possible. Part of Monkey World is devoted to rescued chimpanzees, a five star hotel for creatures that have suffered the worst possible torment at the hands of people. Butch and Charlie were to spend six months in quarantine before joining other rescued chimps in an enormous, exciting wooded sanctuary. Here, for the first time, they could enjoy something like a proper chimp environment.

On the day of release, Butch rushed around his new enclosure. Charlie needed the friendly embrace of keeper Jeremy Keeling to give him enough confidence to fact his new, albeit limited, horizons. "They were so thrilled to be out," said Jane Goodall. "We all had tears in our eyes. At one stage they climbed way up a tall tree and suddenly saw that the ground was so far below them that they froze for a long time, just staring down. Eventually they came down very gradually, the bravest one first."

The situation is not an ideal solution. It would be so much better if the chimps had never been plucked from the wild. Now though, Jane insists we must do our best for them and, who knows, we might even benefit from the contact. Butch and Charlie's story had a happy ending. But there are many Butches and Charlies out there. The chimp watchers have a daunting task ahead of them. There is no doubt that they will continue fighting the battle.

Since *Nature Watch* filmed in Spain, Peggy Templer has died. She was never afraid to challenge photographers, even in the wake of serious threats to her life. Simon has vowed to carry on. "I shall continue the battle, stay on here, and do what I can until the last enemy claims me. Bold words, but I mean them."

Jane Goodall will never stop campaigning for chimpanzees. As she says, "Chimpanzees have given me so much. The long hours spent with them in the forests have enriched my life beyond measure. What I have learnt has shaped my understanding of human behaviour, of our place in nature - and of the chimpanzees place in nature too. I anguish over the suffering that we inflict on so many of them. In the wild their habitat is destroyed; mothers are shot and their infants seized. In captivity they are forced to entertain us; or are imprisoned in the name of science in tiny, barren steel cages. I am haunted by their dull blank eyes, staring out at a world that offers them no hope. The least I can do is to speak out for them. They cannot speak for themselves."

Naturewatcher Erik Zimen, Europe's foremost authority on wolves, with one of the members of his wolf pack

CHAPTER TWO
THE BEST OF FRIENDS?

W ho's afraid of the big, bad wolf? Most of us are, it would seem. Unfortunately for the wolf it is stuck with an evil reputation for nastiness to people, their children, and livestock. The bad press goes back centuries; no other animal has been so enshrined in the myths and legends of northern peoples for its alleged negative qualities. Even today, a host of fictitious images from 'Little Red Riding Hood' to 'An American Werewolf in London' conspire to perpetuate the picture of a manic, sly killer that is bad and dangerous to know.

Fallacious folklore may not strike us as important. It is easy to shrug off the scandalous stories about wolves if you have just enjoyed a *Nature Watch* documentary highlighting the species' true nature. But historically, people have not had such information to hand. They learned about the wolf from tales handed down from generation to generation – perhaps gathered around a spitting log fire in a peasant's humble cottage somewhere in the wooded depths of central Europe, Russia or Canada. The stories were exaggerated with each telling. The people formed fixed opinions which affected their attitudes and actions, and the wolves suffered.

Originally, the grey wolf was the world's most widely distributed mammal after man. It roamed the northern hemisphere from Saskatchewan to Siberia and from Newfoundland Island to Italy, Israel and India. Today that honour goes to another member of the dog family, the red fox. Because of the fear and ignorance nurtured by those old myths, together with habitat loss, the grey wolf has been totally wiped out over much of its former range. The species hangs on precariously in a few large eastern European forests, isolated Mediterranean mountains, semi-desert areas of the Middle East, and wilderness in North America and Asia.

Naturewatcher Erik Zimen is Europe's foremost authority on wolves. He knows, more than anyone, that wolves may be big (they are, in fact, the largest members of the dog family) but they certainly are not bad. He has arrived at this conclusion by the most direct route ... Erik Zimen lives with wolves.

"As a boy, I always wanted to have a dog," says Erik. "My dream was to run with it through the woods around Gothenburg in Sweden where I was raised. But my parents trotted out all the usual excuses that parents say when confronted by a child who wants a dog. They didn't think I was responsible enough to look after it, that sort of thing. Finally, after three years of pleading and begging, they relented. I was allowed to buy my own Airedale terrier called Bonzo. He was a very nice dog and I liked him very much."

It was this early relationship that motivated Erik to return to university after he had completed his degree, and register for a PhD to undertake research on wolves and dogs, and the hybrids between them. This led to a lifetime's preoccupation with wolves that has generated over twenty years of data.

In the village of Peterskirchen in southern Germany where Erik Zimen now lives, he shares his life with numerous animals. As well as ordinary family pets, he has kept about fifty wolves over the years together with Arctic foxes and pine martens.

Keeping the animals has a serious scientific purpose. Most of them are extremely difficult to study in the wild and this is particularly true of shy, secretive wolves. Even in captivity, it takes a long time to win a wolf's trust. But Erik Zimen has come to be accepted by the wolves as a member of their pack. Having made friends with them, he knows that the wolf in reality is not the wicked monster of myth and legend. Its savage persecution at the hands of man is totally unjustified. So Erik decided to tell the truth about wolves to as many people as possible. The most effective way to do that is through TV, so in addition to starring in a *Nature Watch* episode, Erik Zimen has embarked upon a new career in wildlife film making.

The material is all around him. A lot of Erik's understanding of wolves arises out of his daily walks with them through the woods near his home. Walking a pet dog on a leash is one thing, but walks with wolves, untethered and free, are really something special. Erik can only do this because he is an honorary wolf with full pack status. He is not the pack leader, though. That job goes to Raz, Erik's dog and invaluable colleague and companion throughout all the wolf work.

"I always take Raz with me on the wolf walks," says Erik. "He's a terrific wolf guarder. If one of the wolves suddenly runs off, Raz runs up to him or her and then turns around and comes back to me. That motivates the wolf to run back as well. Only with the help of Raz can I let these wolves loose while walking."

By watching them closely every day, Erik learns to interpret many of the subtleties of wolf behaviour. How, for example, they stick together in the open while dispersing when they reach the cover of the forest. He has observed that the pack has a strong hierarchy with a so-called alpha male and alpha female occupying the top positions. Sometimes there is a lower hierarchy among the pups and yearlings, and all the relationships are maintained by a continuous show of strength among the pack's ring leaders.

The alpha male will try to keep his position by dominating the others and advertising his status through various communication signals. Rank is indicated by the position of the tail and body, ears and head. Paw giving and nose nudging are submissive gestures requesting attention. There is a wealth of signalling by smell. All dogs, wild and domestic, urine mark scent posts in their home ranges. The conifer of the wolf is the fabled lamppost of the pet dog. Information in the scent tells other wolves about the age, sex and individual identity of the signaller. Even Erik, in his capacity as canine top dog, has been known to shake a leg and leave a scent as wolf etiquette demands.

When *Nature Watch* filmed Erik Zimen's wolves, one animal, a male called Peter, caused some consternation to Julian Pettifer by continually rubbing his head against the nervous presenter's body. "He's interested in your shampoo," said Erik. "Head rubbing is the beginning of a behavioural sequence called rolling. Wolves often roll in the dung of their prey to mask their characteristic canine odour before going off to hunt. God knows what they want to hunt if they roll in shampoo, though."

Erik Zimen with four of his wolf pack. Erik is accepted as an honorary wolf with full pack status

Wolves often howl to attract a mate: whole packs howl together to attract companions or to warn strangers away from their territory

It is a common misconception that wolves, unlike domestic dogs, do not bark. Erik Zimen has heard many wolf vocalisations and knows that it is not true. "They bark as a warning signal," he says. "If something strange comes along and they're becoming afraid, one or more wolves will bark. It's not very loud but the entire pack hears and takes notice of it."

The most famous wolf noise is howling. Peter often howls to attract a mate but sometimes the whole pack howls together. Erik Zimen thinks this functions as a kind of long distance communication system serving to attract companions or prevent some strange wolf from entering the territory. He further regards it as synchronising behaviour - something to get everyone in the right frame of mind for hunting after a long day's sleep. The pack that howls together stays together and that, according to Erik, is the most important aspect of wolf society. As wolves grow up they are very sociable and strongly bonded to each other. With increasing maturity they also develop a streak of independence and self reliance rarely seen in domestic dogs. If circumstances favour pack hunting, as with Canadian wolves following migrating caribou, the animals stick together to increase their chances of a successful kill. If prey animals are few and far between, the older, more experienced wolves will leave the pack and wander alone for months at a time. Such autonomy earns the wolf great respect from those, like Erik Zimen, who know it as an equal and friend.

For the people who first domesticated dogs from wolves, the 'lone wolf' habit was not an admirable trait. It was a nuisance. No one wanted their animals to stray. So

Wolves are the common ancestor of all the world's breeds of domestic dog

early domestic dog breeding centred around selecting the juvenile wolf features of sticking loyally and dependently to the pack at all times. In that sense, the domestic dog is like a childish wolf.

There are more than four hundred different breeds of domestic dog in the world today; and, incredibly, the common ancestor of them all is the wolf. "Many people find it impossible to believe that every dog from the tiniest Chihuahua to the biggest mastiff could have a single ancestor," says Erik Zimen. "Lots of scientists, even Charles Darwin, suggested that today's wealth and variety of dog breeds could only have evolved from several species including jackals, coyotes and foxes. But all the evidence we have points to the wolf alone."

It is possible that the domestic dog evolved independently several times over from different wolf populations in Europe, North America, Asia and China. Whatever the case, it is clear that the wolf harbours a staggeringly large and varied genetic portfolio, isolated bits of which have been exaggerated and selected for in the development of domestic dog breeds. As Erik Zimen explains: "Every greyhound is much faster than the wolf. Every retriever is much better at retrieving, and any pointer could easily outpoint a wolf."

Such breeds are man made. We have managed to extract specific wolf traits and fine tune them for our convenience and amusement. Sometimes we take it too far. Erik is repulsed and angry with what he terms 'bad breeding'.

"Take the bloodhound," he says. "Its tissues are so weak that all the skin just falls loose on the animal. Then there's the breeds like dachshunds and bassets which people have been making longer and longer so the chest becomes so heavy that the poor dog can hardly walk."

Extreme in-breeding can cause many hereditary defects in domestic dogs. Bulldogs, for example, often have dental and respiratory problems resulting in breathing difficulties due to their compressed noses and jaws. Many of them cannot copulate. The females require Caesarean sections to give birth and no longer look after their pups. Pekingese and Chihuahuas are susceptible to eye injury because their eyes protrude like grotesque gargoyles.

As well as ill health, bad breeding can also lead to bad behaviour. Widespread public concern about killer or so-called 'devil dogs' is not just something whipped up by the tabloid press. There are some breeders who deliberately set out to 'manufacture' the most aggressive and powerful animals possible – ones that cannot be trusted, particularly with children. There has been a great deal of attention paid to Rottweilers in this respect, something that Erik Zimen thinks is unfair to the dogs themselves.

"It's the fault of the Rottweiler breeders and keepers," he says. "The breeders breed what the buyers want. Some people take pride in having a dog that is as aggressive as possible. Such dogs are walking time bombs – one day or another they will get into trouble.

"The same is true of the pit bull terrier. There's always an up and coming breed to occupy the niche of this year's macho dog. German shepherds were in that position fifty years ago. Now breeders are trying to change them back into a friendly family dog."

Man's association with the dog goes back a long way. It is likely that the dog was the first animal to be domesticated – ten thousand years ago that special friendship with people was already established. Erik Zimen has long speculated about the beginnings of the bond between man and dog. He reasoned that although we would never really know how it developed, it might be possible to shed some light on the matter by studying the role of dogs in a tribal society. Accordingly, he travelled to Africa.

"Nobody could understand why I wanted to go on safari and study domestic dogs when there are so many wild animal species on the African savannahs," says Erik. "But the dog has always been a part of human society and nobody has really bothered to study that relationship in a historical perspective."

Erik found what he was looking for among the Turkana people in northern Kenya. There, the basenji has a special role. Basenjis are lightly built dogs with wrinkled foreheads, pricked ears and a tightly curled tail. The breed that does not bark originates from Zaire in central Africa.

To the men of the Turkana, having dogs around the place meant nothing. "If you asked them whether or not they kept a dog, they looked disgusted," says Erik. "Ask them if they kept cows on the other hand and their faces would light with pride. Sheep and goats were less important but they would still be proud of having many."

Among the tribe, the dogs were most important to the women. "One of the first functions of a dog in human society is as a nappy," explains Erik. "A sort of Pampers for early man. When the Turkana baby defecates, the mother makes a t-t-t-t sound

Turkana mother from northern Kenya with baby, child and basenji dog. The dog was probably the first animal to be domesticated

and immediately the dog, who is sleeping in the vicinity, sense an opportunity to eat. It rushes in and cleans up everything very neatly."

Above all, the dog has been man's hunting companion. Both wolf and early people were hunters who worked in teams and, by the end of the Ice Age, the house wolf or early domesticated dog had formed with man a single hunting team.

Erik Zimen thinks that, at the time, new techniques emerged for killing quarry. Techniques like the bow and arrow which tends to injure rather than kill prey. "This is when the house wolves suddenly became valuable," says Erik. "They would chase a wounded rodent and pin it down until the hunter could come in closely and kill it off with his sword."

Such actions are part of the normal sequence of wolf hunting behaviour that Erik Zimen has observed many times in his own animals. "When we go walking with the wolves, they are first out running and trying to find something," he says. "Eventually they find, say, a rodent and test it for speed. After deciding that one or two animals are too fast to bother with, they chance upon an animal they think they can catch and go in for it. There's a short chase, an attack, a kill by biting and a meal that can be gulped down by the hunter or carried to the pups."

When people first started to keep sheep, they needed different kinds of dogs. Purely hunting dogs were out of the question because they would kill all the sheep.

What was needed was a breed or breeds who could adapt the ability of a dominant wolf to keep his pack together. The new herding dogs also inherited the lookout behaviour of wolves, being efficient guarders of the sheep against strangers. If you watch a competent sheep dog working, it is noticeable how the animal may nip his charges to keep them together in a flock, but the bite is always restrained.

Erik Zimen considers it remarkably ironical that people can live with bits of wolf behaviour in isolation. Indeed we depend on them. Convenience packages of specific wolf behavioural traits contained within domestic dog bodies help all sorts of people from the police to polar explorers, and from farmers to the armed forces. What we have not been able to do is to live with the whole wolf in its natural habitat.

Nowhere is this more the case than in Europe. The species is extinct in central Europe and, although the exact date is uncertain, was wiped out in Britain by the middle of the eighteenth century. Sweden and Norway contain less than ten wolves between them. Only in the eastern European countries of Poland, Rumania, Bulgaria, Yugoslavia and European Russia do wolf populations reach one thousand or more.

In Italy, only a couple of hours drive from Rome, Naturewatcher and wildlife biologist Luigi Boitani has been studying wolves for the last nineteen years. His study area is the Abruzzo National Park, fifty-seven thousand hectares of precipitous mountains, forested slopes and alpine meadows that are home to most of Italy's remaining two hundred and fifty wolves as well as brown bears, golden eagles and chamois.

Turkana child with basenji puppy

Naturewatcher Luigi Boitani studies wolves in Abruzzo National Park in Italy

You could walk around the Abruzzo for years and never encounter a wolf. "The chances of seeing one are less than one in a million," says Luigi Boitani. "Not only because there are so few wolves but also because they are very, very wary; very scared and very shy. They have learned that humans are extremely dangerous and are, in the main, adept at avoiding contact."

Because wolves are so elusive, studying their behaviour at close quarters and filming them can only be achieved by keeping them in large enclosures like those of Erik Zimen. It is possible to learn about their distribution, daily wanderings and feeding habits in the wild through the use of radio telemetry.

It was Erik Zimen who first engaged Luigi Boitani on the long term wolf study. Both men had to trap the wolves before they could get anywhere near them. Erik taught Luigi how to outwit the wily wolves of the Abruzzo and eventually they captured several animals.

After being anaesthetised, the wolves were thoroughly examined and fitted with radio collars that could enable them to be radio tracked for long periods over a wide area. Only by building up detailed information was it possible to take steps to conserve the remaining population. Largely thanks to Luigi's efforts Italy's wolves are now protected.

He takes no personal credit for this. Luigi believes that the wolf has only survived in Italy because it has adapted its lifestyle to the human activities around where it lives. "They know when they can travel. They know when they have to hide away," he says. One particular female proved the point.

"She was in Maella region and we were tracking her every night," says Luigi. "She always walked along the same path to her main feeding site, a rubbish dump. At one point the path crossed a paved road, so we parked the car there, kept quiet and aimed to turn our headlights on her when the radio signal indicated that she was about to cross the road."

Events did not go as planned. The wolf arrived at the road and stayed at the edge without crossing. Somehow she sensed that the wolf watchers were there. There began a psychological game of cat and mouse. She waited. Luigi waited. An hour passed, then an hour and a half. Finally, the scientists got tired first and drove home. "As we left, you could see her in the back mirror crossing the road," says Luigi. "Amazingly she knew that white lights are dangerous but red lights mean it is safe to cross."

Experiences like this, coupled with the scenic beauty of Abruzzo in springtime when the snows melt and a profusion of alpine flowers cover the meadows, have drawn Luigi back to his studies year after year.

"In the beginning, my interest in wolf biology was purely academic," he says. "But when you start following and tracking the animals continuously, living so close to them, your attitude widens. The fascination becomes emotional. I couldn't resist going on and on with the research. We will never match the way the wolf copes with this environment. This is what keeps me going. It's certainly not being outside at twenty below in the mountains at the dead of night ... not seeing anything and just feeling cold, damp and wet!"

As he spent more time studying them, Luigi Boitani's interest in wolves grew from being purely academic to a fully emotional attachment to these beautiful animals

For generation after generation, the shepherds of the Abruzzo and their sheep have lived alongside the wolves. Both are aided and protected by the shaggy white Abruzzo sheep-dog and a motley collection of wolf-like looking mongrels used as herding dogs. The latter are very suspicious and aggressive. They hate people but love sheep. Over the centuries the shepherds have bred these characteristics into them by sorting through each litter and selecting the pups that show signs of guarding, rather than killing the sheep.

Each morning the ewes are milked to supply the cheese that supports the shepherds, their families, and the dogs. Somehow the raffish collection of ill tempered dogs survive on a diet of whey, a by-product of the cheese making.

There is an interesting convergence among European sheepdogs in mountainous areas. Pyrenean guard dogs, Abruzzo dogs (the Mare M'Abruzzo), Tatra mountain shepherd dogs and Turkish shepherd dogs all look very similar. The shepherds of these places, though separated by thousands of kilometres, have independently arrived at similar solutions to common problems. They are also steeped in wolf folklore and talking to them has played an important part in helping Luigi Boitani to sort out the uneasy relationship between wolf, man and dog.

Through the discussions and by hearing old stories, Luigi has not found any authenticated cases of wolf attacks upon people. Over the centuries, rabies has come through the area several times, and it is possible that a rabid wolf, like any animal crazed by the virus, could attack a human. Stories then, of course, become exaggerated.

Another factor is the Black Death and periods of warfare when bodies were stacked outside in the open. Wolves, like many creatures, will scavenge and could acquire a taste for such gruesome easy pickings.

Historically though, red deer and roe deer were the favoured prey of the Abruzzo wolves who at the time lived in larger packs than today and could cooperate to bring down the larger game. Then, at the turn of the century, overgrazing and a growing number of sheep displaced the deer. The wolves turned to livestock and sometimes the reputation of the indiscriminate killer was justified.

"Imagine three or four wolves jumping into a sheep pen," says Luigi Boitani. "Like a fox in a chicken run they would kill until the last animal. It's exactly the same behaviour. Domestic livestock tends to stay put and predators are programmed to kill them. The wolves wouldn't benefit much from this. When the shepherd came screaming with his dogs, the wolves would run off, having only had the chance to eat one or two kills."

Nevertheless, such behaviour led to a concerted effort to destroy the Italian wolves. Farmers were invited to pay their taxes in wolf heads and skins rather than hard cash. Professional wolf hunters or Lupari sprang up and every village in the Abruzzo had one. The Lupari were not paid by the government. They were self employed and toured the villages, carrying a dead wolf on their donkeys. Grateful locals gave them cheeses, hams and sausages.

But the Lupari were motivated by self interest. They knew that, by destroying all the wolves, they would do themselves out of a livelihood. Thus, they often left litters untouched and this, together with a somewhat ambiguous local attitude towards wolves (the Abruzzo people could not summon up enough hatred to mount an extermination campaign), resulted in the species' survival in Italy to the present day.

Today the main threat to the Abruzzo wolf comes from its descendant, the domestic dog. Paradoxically, we have created the canine equivalent of Frankenstein's monster. Around every town and village in the Abruzzo has gathered a pack of vagrant dogs with varying degrees of dependence on people. If a dog is born out in the wild and does not meet humans for its first few months, then it becomes feral for life.

Luigi Boitani's project is increasingly concerned with feral dog biology. He has found that wolves and dogs compete for the same resources of space, food and mates. "If you have a group of twenty dogs in a certain area of the mountains, wolves would be afraid to move in," he says. "Then there is interbreeding. It mostly happens when a female wolf is thrown out of the pack. She comes on heat and a big dog mates with her. The litter contains pups that look either like wolves or dogs or any combination thereof. Often they look like dogs but behave like wolves so no one takes any notice until they start killing livestock."

Most of the dogs and wolves feed at the many rubbish dumps in the area where there is enough food to support untold numbers of them. Wolves are more fearful and shy. They do not come down to the dumps as often as the more confident dogs. "If you consider that Italy has eight hundred thousand free ranging dogs and two hundred and fifty wolves, you can begin to understand the task we have ahead of us" says Luigi Boitani.

He has tried to trap the dogs, but some are resilient to all efforts to catch them. Shooting is the last resort. Luigi hates this. "I love dogs," he says, "but there is no other way if we really want to solve the problem.

"Then we must close down the dumps. Wildlife, stray and feral dogs all meet there. All sorts of illnesses can be transmitted. Imagine if rabies cropped up again. Can you imagine the human reaction – completely hysterical. They'd be using poison baits and it would kill everything – foxes, dogs and wolves – it would spell the end of the species in Italy."

The predicament of the Italian wolf is all the more tragic in a country whose capital, Rome, was first ruled by King Romulus. Legend has it that, many years earlier, Romulus and his twin brother Remus were reared by a female wolf after being abandoned on the banks of the River Tiber.

But wherever wolves go, the folklore follows. Who's afraid of the big, bad wolf? Certainly not Luigi Boitani or Erik Zimen. They know that the monster of myth likes nothing better than to go for a daily walk and play endless games.

The real Jaws - *a great white shark*

CHAPTER THREE
SELLING THE SHARK

The tropical bay is calm ... too calm. Suddenly a grey triangular fin appears above the water surface and startled surfers head for shore. The fin reappears, this time accompanied by an ominous two tone soundtrack that builds up into a menacing crescendo. As the manic music pulsates faster and faster, the action speeds up. There's a close up of a swimmer's face paralysed and mute with fear, a frenzy of writhing fishy body, and an explosion of blood into the disturbed ocean. Carnage over: a bather has become history, the blood disperses, and the sea returns to an uneasy stillness. Sharks one, humans nil.

In a world that needs monsters, this is the shark as movie star. Like Dracula, Frankenstein and Freddy on Elm Street, the shark has joined a long list of film friends we all love to hate. *Jaws*, the book, has already sold ten million copies and inspired four feature films. Many people have profited from the evil image of sharks.

And what an image. The simple five letter word SHARK is used to describe all kinds of ruthless predators like lawyers, card players and money lenders. This probably reflects our fear of creatures we regard as little more than primitive eating machines. The conventional view is that sharks are always on the lookout for careless swimmers or luckless divers ... just as you thought it was safe to go back into the water.

It is not only the motion picture industry that has distorted our feelings towards sharks. Until recently, surprisingly little was known about most shark species, and whole components of their biology and lifestyle – like their development and reproductive cycles – remain a mystery, even to the scientists.

The problem is that people cannot travel deep down into the oceans and follow sharks every minute of every day. Most of what we know about shark biology comes from individuals caught in beach nets and they may not be representative of the population as a whole. The nets are erected in countries like South Africa and Australia to remove sharks from areas near public beaches. They trap thousands of sharks each year so the bathers remain safe.

This is more than can be said for the sharks. There is overwhelming evidence that shark populations are declining, almost in direct proportion to the growth in fear and hatred they instil in people. Over the past two decades human exploitation of sharks has increased dramatically worldwide. Of the hundreds of known species, probably twenty or so are fished commercially and these are most at risk. No one is predicting mass extinctions but there is growing concern that the loss of such top level predators will have damaging repercussions on marine food chains.

More than ever, sharks need friends. It is not easy to attract the right kind of attention and support when your infamy goes before you. Sharks are not whales, gorillas or elephants – their profile is not majestic, noble or cuddly. It is one thing to raise conservation funds for tigers; try doing it for tiger sharks. Virtually none of the world's conservation organisations have ever mounted a major shark campaign.

But sharks do have their supporters. Naturewatchers Sam Gruber and Neal Watson are both redressing the balance and marketing the shark as an innocent victim of prejudice and persecution. Their approaches differ. Sam is an academic who conducts research on sharks, Neal a diver who takes other divers and tourists to see sharks at close quarters around Caribbean coral reefs. Both do most of their work in the Bahamas. Both are in the business of de-mystification.

Dr Samuel Gruber is professor of marine biology and fisheries at the University of Miami's Rosenstiel School of Marine and Atmospheric Science. His first shark encounter occurred in the late 1950s when, as a pre-medical student, he was chased out of the ocean by a hammerhead shark three and a half metres long. Reasoning that "if something wants to eat me, I'd like to know why", he decided to devote his career to the study of shark biology and behaviour. Sam now spends a lot of his time at the recently-opened biological field station at Bimini in the Bahamas where he runs research and training courses, and can devote his attentions to shark conservation.

There are several hundred species of shark living in the world's seas and oceans. Until recently scientists had classified about three hundred and fifty types. Now, thanks to the beginning of deep sea trawling, the total is around the four hundred mark. "Four hundred success stories," says Sam Gruber.

Sharks are an extremely ancient animal group. With their close relatives, the skates and rays, they split off from the mainstream of vertebrate (backboned animal) evolution around four hundred million years ago. At one stage, say about three hundred and twenty million years ago, sharks were the most abundant and dominant vertebrates in the early seas.

The whale shark is the world's largest fish, and can reach 14 metres in length! However, it poses no threat to humans - it is a filter feeder, which eats only plankton

Even today, they exhibit a vast diversity of body form and function. The world's largest fish is a shark – the whale shark. At fourteen metres long, the gargantuan animal presents a terrifying spectacle, but there is no need to be afraid. Whale sharks are filter feeders – they swim incessantly like a submarine in slow motion, forever feeding on plankton sieved from the sea by modified gill arches that sit in the cavernous mouth. Basking sharks, the second largest fish, are also filter feeders as is megamouth, a four metre long giant with huge mouth. Megamouth was only discovered in the late 1970s when one washed up on a Hawaiian beach. Since then, several individuals, some with mouths measuring eighty centimetres across, have turned up on southern shores. Megamouth's mouth actually lights up and attracts food at depths of up to three hundred metres. This phenomenon, called bioluminescence, is made possible by a profusion of light-producing gut bacteria. The result is a steady supply of jellyfish, plankton and shrimp for megamouth to eat.

At the other end of the scale, some deep water sharks are as small as twenty centimetres. Others are flattened bottom dwellers with compressed teeth for crushing the hard outer skeletons of their shellfish prey. Species like the thrasher have enormously long tails to stun their prey, and the huge fearsome predaceous types have row upon row of large, razor sharp teeth for cutting their prey into bite-sized chunks. Such species may possess up to three hundred teeth at any one time.

The most famous shark is the great white. Growing to over seven metres in length, this is the only shark to feed mainly on marine mammals like small whales and seals.

It is also the species most often cited in reference to shark attacks upon people. John McCosker, the director of San Francisco's famous Steinhart Aquarium, thinks that, when it comes to dinner, the great white cannot distinguish between its usual prey – seals and sealions – from surfers. Using underwater photography, McCosker has demonstrated the similarity in size and shape of seals and surfboard riders when seen from a few metres below the surface. This would be the view of a hungry great white.

Sharks find their food by utilising a number of sensory systems. Most have poor eyesight, but in some species, like the requiem sharks, the sense of sight is equivalent to a human's. A number of species 'taste' the sea bed for prey by using sensory barbels around the mouth. The best developed sense, though, is smell. All sharks possess two bulbous lumps in the brain known as olfactory lobes. These deal with smell and are twice as large as the rest of the brain. Shark nostrils are only concerned with smelling; breathing, as with all fish, takes place through the gills. To demonstrate the sensitivity of sharks to different odours, scientists have discovered that a single shark can detect one part of blood in a million parts of water (about one drop of blood in one hundred and fifteen litres of water).

Two senses that sharks use have no human equivalents. One is called the lateral line system. Sharks have a series of jelly filled canals that run the length of the head and body. The jelly contains sensory receptors sensitive to pressure waves caused by the movements of other animals and the shark itself. On the snout, a number of pits (called the ampullae of Lorenzini after Stefano Lorenzini, a seventeenth century shark

The great white is the most infamous of all sharks. Its usual diet is whales and seals, but it has also been known to prey on man – probably because it mistakes its human prey for seals, especially when they are on surfboards...

biologist) pick up electrical charges from other animals. The pits can detect charges as low as one millionth of a volt – less than that emitted from normal nervous impulses. They are the most powerful electro receptors in the animal kingdom.

So sharks are far removed from the popular image of unthinking, unfeeling killing machines. "That view is neither supported by my research nor that of anybody else who has studied them," says Sam Gruber. "Sharks are different from other fishes. For a start their skeletons have no bones, only gristle or cartilage. They are a highly evolved, extremely well-adapted group of fish. The myth of the mindless eating machine is one that comes to us from the eighteenth century because sharks have the reputation of eating people. They don't have cute smiles like dolphins, and their eyes are not wide and appealing, so the popular press has made them out to be eating machines.

"Of course nothing could be farther from the truth. For instance, our studies here show that lemon sharks follow a specific feeding routine for their entire lives. Unlike a dog, they won't eat until they burst. They typically eat two per cent of their body weight a day, but their feeding routine and metabolism restricts them to one meal every thirty-six hours. You can't overfeed them. If they're satiated and surrounded by food, they won't take any."

Whether or not all shark species have a feeding schedule is unknown. In one of the most bizarre, and dangerous, experiments of all time, John McCosker became the first scientist to drop a thermometer down the throat of a great white shark, a three and a half metre long male living off Dangerous Reef in South Australia. "It's not the sort of animal you can do research on every day," said McCosker after attracting the fish to his boat by pouring blood and horsemeat into the water.

When the great white arrived, McCosker fed it a large tuna in which he had placed a thermometer and telemetric tracker. The latter contained hooks to lodge in the shark's stomach after the tuna had been digested.

The experiment revealed the great white to be a big, clumsy fish barely able to eke out a meal. The species is an opportunistic eater whose prey is only encountered sporadically. In fact, the giant fish may go months without a decent meal, when it survives on reserves stored in the liver.

At those rare times when food does come along – for example, during sealion breeding seasons when the pups take their first hesitant swims – the great white has evolved a mechanism to speed up its digestion rate and store food in the liver to provide an on tap emergency energy source. Evidence from the thermometer revealed that the shark's stomach temperature increased by almost seven degrees centigrade during meal times. This not only speeds digestion but also allows the animal to go back for second helpings in a relatively short space of time. Quite remarkable for a cold blooded animal.

McCosker does not know what causes the stomach temperature to rise. He thinks that muscular contractions warm the blood which is then pumped to the stomach. Stomach lining muscles and a special enzyme system may also be involved.

The whole thing sounds very clever, although it is purely a biological adaptation and not 'clever' in the normal sense of the word. But what about sharks' cleverness? Are they mindless or are they intelligent creatures?

In a dangerous experiment to monitor the movements of great white sharks, John McCosker fed them tuna bait in which he had placed a tracking device

After fifteen years of research on captive sharks, Sam Gruber is still hedging his bets. "There are no rules for defining intelligence in sharks," he says. "It's like asking me to say how many angels you could get on the head of a tin tack. We do know, though, that sharks are extremely easy to train. In my fifteen years studying their eyesight, I've trained them to sort of talk to me. I put them in a maze and, by using classical conditioning techniques, train them to make choices at a door and in a chamber. They have to indicate whether they saw a light or not. Much to my surprise they learn about twice or three times faster than a rabbit under exactly the same conditions. They also forget what they learn less quickly than the rabbit. I'm not saying that sharks are smarter than rabbits, but they're adapted to keep a whole load of things in their head to cope with their way of life."

Sam Gruber reasons that research and education are the keys to "putting sharks in their true perspective and dropping the death fish image". His current studies centre around unravelling the mysteries of shark life histories. "I'm personally interested from an intellectual curiosity point of view," he says, "but, also, if we find out what sharks really do, it will be a big step towards dispelling the ignorance and myths that surround them.

Naturewatcher Sam Gruber uses lemon sharks as a model to discover more about the secret lives of sharks - what they eat, how fast they grow, how many of them there are

"I use the lemon shark as a model," says Sam. "I study all phases of its life history. I want to know what it preys on, what its food intake is, what its energetics are, how fast it grows, how long it lives and how many are swimming around in the oceans. We need hard figures on these things. Then we'll be able to say with real mathematical precision how the shark's life history affects its population biology, ecology and commercial relationship with man."

Shark breeding strategies vary widely between species. Many sharks lay eggs – often in egg cases called mermaids' purses – among seaweeds or in cracks on the ocean floor. Some bear live young and have structures similar to the placenta of mammals. A number produce young that feed off their yolk reserves, whilst others produce unfertilised eggs that nourish embryos in the uterus.

Like many endangered species, sharks are slow to grow and mature. They live a long time and produce relatively few young in a lifetime. This is the K-strategy lifestyle referred to in Chapter 5: *Islands aren't Islands any more*. It's an efficient survival strategy under normal circumstances. Sharks can grow to a large size and invest heavily in a small number of well developed, tough offspring.

Unfortunately, most sharks no longer live under normal circumstances. A hundred million of them are killed each year. "That's the equivalent in weight to seven nuclear aircraft carriers fully loaded with planes and bombs," says Sam Gruber.

The main threat comes from commercial fishermen who either target selected shark species or kill them incidentally whilst going after other fish. "Whenever shark fisheries are directed at a particular species, we see a pattern called boom and bust," explains Sam Gruber. "At first the sharks are easy to catch and the fisheries go wild.

Then after a few years, you can't find them any more. They're caught out and it takes twenty to fifty years for them ever to recover, if indeed they do."

He knows this all too well from bitter experience. For ten years, Sam and colleague Charles Manire captured lemon sharks around Summerland Key in Florida Bay. During the period, the catch-release rate steadily declined from over one hundred and fifty in 1986 to forty-two in 1988 and a mere fourteen in 1989. Comparisons with other research conducted in the same area revealed a similar pattern – the southern Florida Keys population of lemon sharks was definitely disappearing, along with Sam's study programme.

This was not an isolated case. In Ireland, the Achill Island shark fishery had taken small numbers of basking sharks for centuries as they followed their summer migration through local waters. In 1950 a mass slaughter began with the result that, from 1952 to 1964, the annual catch crashed from two thousand to forty-seven individuals. Even today, the world's second largest fish has not returned in significant numbers to its former pastures.

The porbeagle shark was once one of the best known shark species in British waters. Then, in the early 1960s, the Norwegian fishing fleet decimated the population for the Italians who considered the porbeagle a delicacy. In 1968, fishing was discontinued because there were too few sharks left to make it economically viable. Two decades later, the porbeagle population has not recovered.

Shark populations are under a great deal of threat from over-killing by fishermen. Sam Gruber has spent ten years studying the lemon shark in Florida bay – the catch-release rate has shown that the population has been seriously declining during this period

"This destruction seems to be a thing of western – so-called civilised – people," says Sam Gruber. "Sharks are actually revered by the oceanic peoples of Polynesia and Hawaii. We give them a negative image but the facts don't fit the myths. True, in any one year about fifty shark attacks are reported – half of them fatal. But animals like elephants and crocodiles kill many more people than sharks. For every person killed by a shark, we kill four million of them!"

Two things really incense Sam Gruber. One is the use of drift nets that kill millions of sharks, sea birds and marine mammals each year. He likens them to 'walls of death' or 'oceanic plagues'. The other is the heinous practice of 'finning'. That's when sharks are captured, have their fins amputated, and are often returned still alive to a sure death from starvation in the sea. It is done mostly for the oriental market in shark's fin soup "... at the demise of one shark per bowl".

What can be done to turn the tide in the favour of the sharks? Sam Gruber is clear, "get those unselective high seas drift nets off the ocean and you'll stop twenty thousand sharks being killed a week. The United Nations is looking into this but there's still a French fishery operating a drift gill net that's killing blue sharks in the Atlantic at a prodigious rate.

"Ban finning. Have a closed season on sharks. The United States National Marine Fisheries Service has a series of rules on this that will become effective in the next few months. They include a cap on landings in the closed season; a bag limit for sports fishermen, licensing of shark dealers. You know, there'll be a lot of paperwork but the alternative is no sharks in the sea ... mind you, a lot of people think that's a good thing, but believe me it's not."

If shark exploitation goes unchecked, marine food chains will lose a top level predator. No one can predict exactly the effects of this, but there could be an explosion of prey species that literally eat themselves out of the environment. Sam Gruber compares it to mountain lions in the southwestern United States. Until recently, farmers killed the cats to 'protect' their sheep, cattle and big game species. Without their former enemies to keep them under control, the antelope population multiplied beyond the food resources of its habitat.

There still remains the thorny issue of the shark's public image. To improve this, you can make TV programmes (like *Nature Watch*) or write books about them. You can exhibit them in aquaria. Better still, you can introduce people to the real thing.

That's what Neal Watson does. He's a diver with some thirty years diving experience under his belt. Nowadays he takes groups of tourists on organised dives around the Bahamian coral reefs in order to engineer close encounters with the creatures of the deep ... including sharks.

"I first learned to dive in freshwater springs so sharks weren't a concern," says Neal. "When I started diving in the ocean, I was absolutely convinced that the first shark I saw would gobble me up alive."

It was to be two years before that fateful day. "I had the normal diver's reaction ... one of absolute fear," remembers Neal. "I streaked to the boat as fast as possible and, whilst swimming, could see how close on my heels this animal was. Then I realised

Naturewatcher Neal Watson takes tourists on dives around the Bahamian coral reefs to give them a close encounter with sharks

that the shark was probably twice as scared as me, and that he was heading in the other direction."

Neal's fascination with sharks grew when some movie production companies approached his dive operation in the Bahamas looking to hire safety divers. "I got to work with some of the really great shark handlers in the industry and became amazed

Sharks have suffered persecution by man for their Jaws *image which is proving difficult to shake off. This is a sand tiger shark*

at how sensitive these creatures are. It's really difficult to keep them alive in aquaria during filming, and their beauty and grace is such a thrill. If you talk to the average diver, he's been diving for five years all over the Caribbean and has never encountered a shark. For me, and my divers, it has got to the point where we're addicted to our shark encounters."

Neal is aware of the contradiction of, on the one hand, trying to encourage people to like sharks, and on the other, being formerly involved in a business that presents them as monsters. "Well that's show biz ... somebody's got to do it," he laughs. "Mind you, the diving industry went hysterical when the first *Jaws* movie came out. Dive shops were literally going out of business and instruction classes probably dropped off seventy-five per cent. I mean it was such a ridiculous movie in terms of any factual behaviour of sharks. Fortunately, when the sequels came out, they were so bad that suddenly the movie lost credibility and became a joke. The sharks suffered though. Shark teeth jewellery was all the rage and killing a shark became the in thing. The slogan 'the only good shark is a dead shark' created a real problem at the time."

These days Neal is into "giving people the experience of a lifetime – something they'll be able to tell their children and grandchildren". He hopes for a calm sea with almost no current so the visibility will be excellent. Then he goes down into the ocean with a bucket of chum – fish carcasses and heads obtained from fishermen at the local docks.

The divers go down next. They organise themselves into a semicircle behind Neal on a sandbank opposite the coral reef. Safety divers hover with prods above the rookie divers. They're there to make sure the sharks don't get too close and spook the novices. "Probably the greatest danger in this dive would be a diver freaking and coming streaking to the surface with embolism," says Neal.

As the chum is released, the divers wait. First two or three sharks appear – one and a half metre long Caribbean reef sharks. Then a larger bull shark and a spectacularly huge black grouper who appears more interested in the bait than the sharks do. On a typical dive, tourists may encounter at least half a dozen sharks. "It's a very exciting experience," says Neal. "These people will come up with adrenalin pumping like crazy."

The whole event is a great adventure, but Neal Watson also maintains that it is an educational experience. "After you've seen the gracefulness of those creatures, I think you develop more of a respect for the animal than a fear of it. When people begin to understand that all sharks aren't instantly going to kill a diver, it will teach them the fact that the problem they have is all in their mind."

Sam Gruber is ambivalent about diving shark encounters. He acknowledges that close contact can be a powerful conservation awareness tool, but considers that the benefit a small number of people obtain should be balanced against the, albeit very small, possibility that somebody could get bitten. On further reflection, he sides with the divers – "Flying over the reef is a hundred times more dangerous, going in the boat is a thousand times more dangerous and putting the scuba gear on is a million times more dangerous. It's always a good thing when education supplants ignorance."

Neal Watson agrees. "I've had literally thousands of divers in the water over the years and I have yet to encounter one situation where a shark was a threat under normal sport diving circumstances. Of course you have to make sure the sharks don't lose their natural fear of man and it's different in areas where other fish school or are shot. In such feeding grounds, sharks might accidentally mistake a diver for a potential meal. Normally though, sharks are no problem."

The problem is convincing people of that. Both Sam Gruber and Neal Watson feel that sharks have had a raw deal in the past, but Sam, for one, retains an element of hope.

"Compared to whales, sharks are an extremely hard sell. The nightmare horror image has to be turned around. My reading of the situation is that, through education, through television, people are beginning to separate the myth from the reality. They're starting to understand the ecological role of sharks in marine environments. A significant movement towards a conservation ethic for sharks has finally begun."

Many people have are scared of snakes – this fear and the resulting persecution has made humans a great threat to these beautiful animals. This is a vine snake

GIVING THE SNAKE AN EVEN BREAK

A re you scared of snakes? Many people are. Ironically, it is the fear of snakes that makes humans much more dangerous to them than vice versa. Whenever people and snakes – or indeed reptiles generally – live alongside each other, trouble is almost certain, and more often than not it's the reptiles that lose out. People have always eyed snakes with prejudice and have persecuted them as a result. Perhaps it all started in the garden of Eden with Adam, Eve, an apple and a serpent a.k.a. the old devil himself.

Much of the prejudice and persecution is encountered in tropical countries. This is not because the people there are necessarily any more prejudiced or persecution-minded than elsewhere, but because most reptiles inhabit hot places. It's all to do with temperature control.

One of the great biological misnomers is the phrase 'cold blooded'. It's biologically inaccurate – cold blooded animals don't have cold blood under normal circumstances – and culturally loaded. Terms like 'murder in cold blood' or 'cold blooded killer' imply a hard, unfeeling psychopathic situation or person. Herpetologist Romulus Whitaker has studied reptiles for most of his life. He describes reptiles as 'ectotherms', a word meaning 'outside heat'.

What this means is that reptiles and other ectotherms have to get their heat, and hence energy, from outside the body. Unlike warm blooded (or endothermic) mammals and birds, they cannot control their body temperature by shovelling in food energy and adjusting their physiology like an internal thermostat. Reptiles rely on the sun and adjust their behaviour to stay at the right temperature to go about their business. They bask on rocks to warm up; and seek shade, shelter or a nearby pond to cool down.

With this dependence on external heat sources, it's not surprising that the greatest diversity of reptiles is found in the warmer countries. This also attracts a great diversity of reptile watchers like Romulus Whitaker, an American whose life's work has centred around dispelling misinformation about snakes and conserving all reptiles in India.

The Indian subcontinent is a vast mosaic of habitats that runs from the Himalayas in the north to Cape Comorin in the south, a length exceeding 3,000 kilometres. The total area is nearly five million square kilometres – about the size of western Europe. India contains at least 45,000 plant species organised into fifteen distinct climatic zones. From tropical evergreen forest to dry lands and alpine areas to coastal wetlands, the climate is largely influenced by

Naturewatcher Romulus Whitaker is an American living in India where he has spent his life conserving snakes and other reptiles. Here he is feeding a mugger

the incidence of monsoons. Each vegetation type supports distinctive wildlife communities including a vast array of reptiles.

Two hundred and thirty-six snake species, about one tenth of the Earth's total, live in India. These range from the world's largest – the reticulated python at about eleven metres three times as long as a normal family saloon car – to finger length worm snakes. About a quarter of them (55 species) are venomous including the cobra, krait, Russell's and saw-scaled vipers.

"India's full of snakes," says Rom Whitaker. "It's full of snake lore and snake legends, snake charmers, snake carvings and temples. But the majority of it is totally based on mystical lore and myths. It all adds up to totally misleading facts about snakes. It's mind boggling to see how much misinformation is around in a land which is so full of these creatures."

Romulus Whitaker arrived in India from America over forty years ago. He settled among the Irula people – a tribal minority of hunter gatherers with a history of snake hunting. Now endangered themselves, the Irula's skills and knowledge have blended with Whitaker's maverick panache in the cause of conservation.

Known locally as Pambukuran or Snakeman, Rom Whitaker's clever and creative utilisation of wildlife has met the daunting challenge of Indian environmental management head on. Conservation in the subcontinent is overshadowed by the growing needs of 800 million people; by the mounting pressure on land for food and

About one tenth of the world's total snake species live in India and the country is full of snake lore - these are snake carvings on fertility stones

Many venomous snakes like this Russell's viper live in rice fields, and as 80 per cent of Indian people live in rural villages and go barefoot, snake bites are common and the fear of snakes great. Many of the snakes are actually beneficial, however, preying on the rats that consume the farmers grain

industry that's evident everywhere. You have to possess a single minded doggedness of herculean proportions to remain optimistic and constructive in the face of all that. Rom Whitaker does. He has a bedrock of burning commitment that began when he was a small boy on the east coast of the United States.

"I was about five years old in a little town way up north in New York State. I began catching garter snakes, and I had my own little aquarium or terrarium."

None of Rom's family were interested in reptiles but they encouraged the boy to develop his hobby. "I think it's just that at that age you're interested in a hell of a lot of little creatures of all kinds. Gradually, one by one, you're discouraged from being interested in each one as it goes up the line. I mean insects, OK, but don't graduate to snakes. Don't bring a frog home in your pocket. Eventually I think kids get discouraged but I never was."

When he was eight years old, Rom left the relative paucity of New York's reptile species to settle in the subcontinent. Stepping off the plane, assimilating the tropical sights, sounds and smells, and discovering a whole new world of scaly abundance, the young Whitaker never looked back.

"Yeah, it's sort of like graduating," he remembers fondly. "I mean it was garter snakes and here suddenly it was cobras, rat snakes and vipers. Of course I didn't start right away into that league but by the time I was probably twelve or thirteen I was getting into the so-called hot snakes, and I'm probably really lucky to be here. You're foolish when you're twelve, thirteen years old and I'm sure I must have made all sorts of potentially deadly mistakes."

Deadly mistakes happen often enough in India's rice fields. As eighty per cent of Indian people live in rural villages and go barefoot, it is not surprising that snake bites are fairly common. About 9,000 people die horrifically from snake bite each year. Rice fields are particularly promising habitats for kraits, cobras and Russell's vipers that prey on the rats that consume the farmer's rice.

This is not to suggest that rice fields are the killing fields of India. Most snakes are, in fact, harmless, shy, localised in distribution and only bite if surprised or in self-defence. Three-quarters of snake bites in India occur at night and 90 per cent of venomous bites inject too little venom to be lethal. To put snake bite incidence into perspective, consider this: in a recent year Bombay hospitals admitted four people for snake bite and 20,000 for rat bite.

Nevertheless the fear of snakes is the biggest stumbling block to their conservation. Often any snake seen is instantly killed by any weapon close at hand. Some groups, however, use snakes in religious ceremonies .

The indiscriminate killing of snakes robs India of important rodent predators. It is said that without mongooses, owls and snakes, India could not feed itself. One FAO (Food and Agricultural Organisation of the United Nations) report suggested that rats ate the same amount of grain per year as was imported under various foreign aid schemes – perhaps up to one quarter of the total grain production.

On his early explorations through the rice fields, Rom Whitaker first encountered the Irula tribal people who made their living as snake catchers supplying ten million snakeskins a year to make shoes and handbags. Rom has now found a way of using traditional Irula snake catching skills. It's an ingenious scheme that conserves the snake but also helps combat the dreadful mortality from snake bite.

"As far as we know there are 28,000 Irulas," says Whitaker. "I don't know how many of them are involved in snake catching, but probably at least five or ten thousand. I've had experience in other countries where people catch snakes but I've never seen people who know that much in depth about snakes as the Irulas do. To me they're probably the most skillful snake catchers anywhere in the world.

"It's hard to say exactly when it began but we've traced it back a bit – perhaps three generations to the beginning of the snakeskin industry. The Irulas were convinced that they had remedies against snake bite which they do, they have herbal remedies, and so they were the only people who could get into snake hunting with any degree of confidence that they weren't going to get killed by a snake. Inevitably they became the main suppliers to the snakeskin industry."

India was once the most important Asian exporter of snakeskin. Following concern about the explosion of rodent populations with attendant crop damage, and the extermination of local snake populations, legislation concerning snake exploitation came into force in 1968. Further legislation followed and the trade was banned in 1976. Today it is illegal to export reptile skins from India.

However, a 1988 report by the wildlife agency TRAFFIC noted that the smuggling

The Irula tribal people used to supply ten million snakeskins a year to make shoes and handbags. India was once the most important Asian exporter of snakeskin, but it is now illegal to export reptile skins

of skins out of India, both by tourists and as an illicit skin trade, continued to flourish. Seven snake species are listed on Appendix two of the Convention on International Trade in Endangered Species (CITES) which has reduced importations in some consumer countries. Large stockpiles of snakeskins remain within India and act as a cover for the illegal trade. Only the Indian python is known to be directly threatened by illegal trade although much more research is needed to ascertain effects on other species.

Romulus Whitaker was involved in attempts to halt the snakeskin industry right from the beginning. As he says "We were always putting in the word on various snake species to the government, recommending the closure of the industry, and campaigning." He knew that a trade ban would have drastic effects on the Irulas and, indeed, it did. A lot of them were left starving after the snake skin industry folded.

The fact that the Irulas were going through a hard time made Romulus Whitaker think that he ought to do something to help them. Working in close conjunction,

Whitaker and the Irulas came up with the idea of snake venom extraction. They would capture the snakes, milk the venom and release the snakes. Then they could sell the venom, making a profit out of the operation without harming the animals.

This has proved to be financially successful. Rom Whitaker is the technical adviser but, by and large, the business is run by Irulas. At the moment only a few hundred families are benefiting from the scheme, out of the thousands of Irula families out there. Still, it is a start – the only income that these people are likely to come by, and for a tribe which was not used to any cash income it has proved vital.

The remedy for snakebite, anti-venom serum made from snake venom, was discovered nearly a century ago. Even today it often fails to reach the poor Indian villager who's the most common victim of snakebite. Russell's viper, named after the

The Irula people suffered greatly after the destruction of the snakeskin industry. Now they catch the snakes alive in order to milk their venom which can be sold. This man is digging for cobra

Venom is being extracted from this Russell's viper to make anti-venom serum and for medical research. Venom is extracted three times, then the snake is released back into the wild

eighteenth century English herpetologist Patrick Russell, saw-scaled viper, spectacled cobra, krait and other common venomous snakes of the ricefield are most in demand for venom extraction. All of these are collected by the members of the Irula snake catchers co-operative. Rom Whitaker explains what happens:

"Well, the snakes are caught and brought to the co-operative. The venom is only extracted three times, once a week for three weeks. Then the snake's released back to the wild. This is the only venom production centre doing this. Of all the centres I've ever seen or worked in, anywhere in the world, this is the only one that doesn't keep the snakes until they die.

"Everywhere else the snakes normally have a very premature death within three to six months of capture. They just can't stand being handled all the time for venom extraction."

The Irula co-operative has been supplying almost all the venom requirements for the production of anti-venom serum in India as well as venom for medical research. As Rom Whitaker explains:

The Madras Snake Park was first opened in 1969 and over one and a half million visitors a year used to go to learn about snakes

"There's been a lot of work on the isolation of some of these toxins to use in surgery. Some venoms clot blood so they use it in dental surgery. Some can actually dissolve clots and thrombosis in people's bodies. And there are some venoms like the neurotoxins produced by kraits and cobras that have been used to treat pain, spinal tuberculosis, migraine and some forms of cancer."

When the snakes are returned to the wild, they are never released near villages or in the ricefields where they were captured. "We put them in the reserve forests bordering the agricultural areas," says Rom. "They still migrate back to the fields though."

Romulus Whitaker strongly believes in the impact of using live animals to disseminate conservation education messages. As a confirmed exponent of the "putting your money where your mouth is" school of doing things, he leased an abandoned building site some thirty kilometres south of Madras in 1969. Within a short space of time, a series of thatched enclosures had been constructed and a brightly coloured sign adorned the entrance. The Madras Snake Park was born.

It was not an auspicious start, and the Park limped along on a shoestring for the first few years. Not many visitors came and those who did frequently sneaked under the perimeter fence without forking out the 25 paise admission charge. Once in, the captive audience were exposed to the gospel of herpetology according to Rom Whitaker. The Snake Park's two staff repeated the same messages over and over: that there are only four common dangerous groups of snakes in India; that these snakes will only bite if stepped on or injured; and that, if administered promptly, anti-venom serum is a one hundred per cent effective cure for snake bite.

The latter idea was still revolutionary to many rural Indians. Rom's staff had to use a bit of persuasion to get it across. By all means use herbal medicines, visitors were told – but only use them on your way to hospital. Also, because the snake gives you an injection of venom, you must get an injection to be cured.

Gradually, news of the Snake Park spread. Journalists came and wrote articles about the crazy American snake man who swore in fluent Tamil. When Rom returned from the forests of Agumbe with two king cobras he caught in a sleeping bag, the fame of the Park was assured.

However, despite an annual five thousand rupee grant from World Wildlife Fund India the place was still in dire financial straits. It probably would have closed, but at the eleventh hour the Tamil Nadu Forest Department very generously leased it half a hectare of land in the beautiful Guindy Deer Park of central Madras.

The revamped and relocated Madras Snake Park opened its gates in 1971, and soon after formed a trust for public education and reptile conservation. The early 1970s were spent building and rebuilding – forever experimenting with enclosures that suited the animals, satisfied the visitor's curiosity and stood up to the hot Madras climate. The only minor criticism came from the Irulas – the move into the city meant they had to undertake a long bus ride from their tribal homes, and that is not easy when your arms are full of muslin bags bursting with snakes.

Some one and a half million annual visitors used to wander round and hear lectures at the Snake Park. There was an education programme for school children, the nucleus of a research unit, and a library. Large, environmentally controlled terraria housed the bigger species, and colleagues and students visited from all over India and the rest of the world. In 1984, Rom Whitaker hosted the first meeting of the World Conservation Union (IUCN) Snake Specialist Group at the Park.

From early on in the Park's development, Romulus Whitaker resolved to devote half his time to field studies. With the Irulas he mounted a series of expeditions to the Western Ghat hills of South West India. Those trips resulted in the discovery of vital information about threatened rainforest areas, and laid the foundation for future research and conservation measures.

Zai Whitaker, Rom's wife, believes that the early expeditions were typical of the spirit of the trust. "One of the strengths of the Snake Park," she has written, "was to develop projects and then turn them over to institutions with better facilities." A case in point was the olive ridley turtle egg collecting programme.

Olive ridley sea turtles nest on most of the mainland Indian beaches, but exceptionally large numbers come ashore every February on a ten kilometre stretch of beach in the Bhitar Kanika Wildlife Sanctuary in Orissa. The spectacle is known as 'arribada' (from the Spanish for 'the coming'). As many as two hundred thousand turtles vie for space to lay their eggs; sometimes accidentally digging up other turtle eggs as they do so. During the turtle breeding season, Rom and Zai Whitaker used to take long beach walks. They were invariably overtaken by commercial egg collectors and figured that most of the eggs ended up in the local market if they hadn't already been eaten by scavenging dogs and jackals. Using a friend's seaside compound, they began a turtle hatchery and sent out regular volunteer teams at night to collect eggs.

Sometimes the tireless volunteers walked for fifteen to twenty kilometres a night, but it paid off. In 1977 Rom's turtle snatch squad collected fourteen thousand eggs and released nine thousand hatchlings. They then turned the project over to the Central Marine Fisheries Research Institute where it is now an annually budgeted central government activity. By 1983, the Tamil Nadu Forestry Department had begun to organise turtle beach patrols and collections for the hatcheries.

Unable to stand still, Romulus Whitaker had, by this time, turned his attentions to another group of rare reptiles, the crocodilians.

Drive south from Madras and before long you'll encounter the Crocodile Bank and the hordes of visitors who now pour through its gates every day of the year. Although it has become a tourist attraction, it's not a zoo. When Rom started it in 1975, it was a desperate measure to save India's dwindling crocodilians, a gene bank on which to draw in the future.

The Rom and his colleagues had conducted crocodilian censuses from the saddle of motor cycles since the early 1970s. Rom Whitaker points out that, "at that stage it was really a critical time for crocodiles in India and elsewhere. It was very important that we publicised and brought alive the concept of keeping crocodiles for perpetuity - in other words create a genetic bank for them."

Anyone spending a few moments in the company of Romulus Whitaker will soon

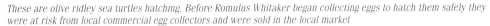

These are olive ridley sea turtles hatching. Before Romulus Whitaker began collecting eggs to hatch them safely they were at risk from local commercial egg collectors and were sold in the local market

This is a mugger being fed at the Crocodile Bank - a gene bank set up in 1975 to save India's dwindling population of crocodilians

The largest of the three crocodilians found in India, male salt water crocodiles may exceed six metres in length and weigh over one tonne. This is an endangered species in the wild as its natural habitats are disappearing

realise that he's an out and out croc freak. "This is a hundred million year old animal that can live for almost a century. That makes it ancient in both respects - and it's just so damned impressive. People are impressed by different things and people are impressed by people who talk well or who look well. I'm just very impressed by crocodiles in the same sense. They're just real people to me."

India has three crocodilians; the mugger, the saltwater or estuarine crocodile, and the gharial. Muggers or marsh crocodiles are broad snouted stocky animals formerly common in lowland river systems throughout the Indian subcontinent. Today, viable populations probably only live in India and Sri Lanka. They nest in riverbank holes and maintain a strict social hierarchy with large males dominating other animals.

Saltwater crocodiles are the largest crocodilians. Mature males may exceed six metres in length and weigh over a tonne. The species has a widespread distribution, occurring throughout southern and south-east Asia and Australasia. This is the crocodile of Crocodile Dundee fame. Large individuals occasionally become man-eaters and the reptile is responsible for around 50-100 deaths worldwide a year. Despite this, and because of its disappearing habitat, the species is classified as endangered by the World Conservation Union.

Rom Whitaker says that salties are definitely more aggressive than other crocodilians. Or, as he puts it, 'defensive'. "People get the wrong impression with the word 'aggression'."

Gharials are large, slender-snouted fish-eaters named after the pot-like structure on the adult male's snout (the word 'ghara' means 'pot' in Hindi). Rom thinks its function is to attract the females ("they certainly create a very interesting profile on the water with this big lump"). Gharials are largely confined to Himalayan fed rivers in the northern part of the subcontinent. By 1974, the total world wild population was estimated at fewer than one hundred and fifty, of which one hundred were in India. Today, over eleven hundred animals have been returned to former wild haunts.

The decline of wild crocodilians in India was due to a combination of factors. "I think it was that they were all killed for their skins," says Rom Whitaker. "Added to that, local people often killed them for meat and collected the eggs to eat. One time that might have been OK, but as numbers were so low it was a critical time for the crocs. The biggest factor, though, is just that their habitats were going through all sorts of changes."

The Crocodile Bank has bred and reared all three Indian crocodilian species. Mugger breed each year and over 9,500 have been produced. Estuarine crocodiles first bred there in 1983 – an Indian captive first. The Bank has supplied over five hundred young crocodiles to Indian government rearing and release projects.

Now Rom Whitaker has gone international: "When we started, the Croc Bank was

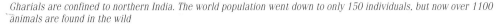

Gharials are confined to northern India. The world population went down to only 150 individuals, but now over 1100 animals are found in the wild

intended only for Indian crocs, and then we decided that there's a lot of other endangered crocs in the world, and the whole concept of the Bank could be broadened to include breeding groups or gene pools of every species. We started accumulating exotic species like the South American spectacled caiman, and now we have ten species here."

Rom Whitaker started with thirty to thirty five crocodilians. Now the Bank has over ten thousand. "They breed like proverbial rabbits. Anywhere else, crocs won't even lay one nest; here many of them lay two clutches a year. This year we expect another six thousand eggs. Our backyard is full of them. I mean, we're surrounded by them. It's getting a little embarrassing to figure out how to feed them." How on earth do you feed ten thousand ravenous crocodiles? Romulus Whitaker hit upon a brilliant solution. It was back to his good friends, the Irulas.

The Irulas are very good at catching rats as well as snakes, and rats can be fed to crocodiles. Farmers have traditionally paid Irulas to come during the harvest season and catch rats. The rodents are field rats – clean and relatively disease free denizens of the rice fields. They're an excellent source of protein yet incredibly destructive. Every captured rat may leave behind a burrow stuffed with up to five kilograms of rice.

The Irula rodent control programme is supported by the Indian government. Twenty or thirty Irulas go out into the fields every day and, between them, may capture up to ninety thousand rats a season. Most of these are then sold to Rom Whitaker as 'croc meals'.

The great snake man thinks that this is the way forward. He wants to create a closed cycle system involving rat catching, croc farming and snake venom extraction. The whole thing would be very nicely balanced and reciprocal. No species would become endangered and the Irulas would make a decent living.

"Sometimes the whole thing seems so gradual and so slow and painstaking, but there's a lot of good feeling towards what we're doing," says Romulus Whitaker. "It gives me a very optimistic feeling that the Irulas can do again what they did traditionally, but towards a positive cause."

This is Kali, from the Irula tribe. Farmers pay the Irula people to catch the rats which destroy their rice crops. Many of these rats are then sold on to Romulus Whitaker to feed his crocodilians at the Crocodile Bank

Many oceanic islands are no longer idyllic for their natural inhabitants. Humans have introduced diseases, predators and pests that threaten the future of the island wildlife. This is Mauritius, home of Naturewatcher Carl Jones

CHAPTER FIVE
ISLANDS AREN'T ISLANDS ANY MORE

"No man is an island," wrote John Donne, one of England's greatest poets. Maybe not, but many people would love to escape to a tropical paradise island for at least part of the time ... away from the hustle and bustle of city life and the dreaded rat race. Away from it all; no pressures, no problems, no worries.

However, safe, secluded islands with strange, unique plants and animals are increasingly a thing of the past. Even vast oceans are no longer effective barriers to invading alien influences – animals, plants, even toxins and pollutants. Too many people have already 'got away from it all' on such islands. Too many people have brought their pigs, dogs, goats and chickens to wreak havoc in numerous oceanic idylls. Too many people have introduced diseases, predators and pests such as rats, cats and mongooses that ring the death toll for native faunas anywhere an outcrop of rocks emerges from the sea. Islands simply aren't islands any more.

Naturewatchers Carl Jones and Don Merton have both found their fantasy islands to be somewhat different from the holiday brochures. Carl works in Mauritius and Don spends his time flitting between mainland New Zealand and its associated offshore islands as well as other Pacific and Indian Ocean islands. Despite being ensconced in different oceans, climates and time zones, the two men have encountered a remarkably similar set of problems that threatens their respective havens. Both have responded in novel and innovative ways, but the end results are always the same - species once thought to be past the point of no return make a comeback. Endangered birds (one of the animals that both men specialise in) fly, hop, waddle, feed, nest and breed again in their rightful homes.

The actual numbers of birds on islands is small, but island birds are often endemic – unique to that island. Islands comprise only about 3 per cent of the Earth's land mass, but over 90 per cent of recorded bird extinctions were island birds, and about 53 per cent of endangered birds are island forms.

Oceans form barriers around islands, discouraging influxes of new, would-be colonists. They also encourage the residents to stay put – indeed many island birds have lost the ability to fly in the absence of predators, and thus are now poor dispersers. Isolated populations often diverge rapidly from their mainland relatives, and new species are formed. Being cut off led to the quick (in evolutionary terms) development of

Many island birds have filled the ecological niches which elsewhere are occupied by mammals. Kiwis, with their long probing beaks and excellent sense of smell, are the equivalents of small insectivorous animals like shrews and hedgehogs

Because they have evolved over millions of years without encountering man or any other mammalian predators or competitors New Zealand's native birds are terribly vulnerable to introduced predators. This is the first and last photo of Stead's bush wren, sadly now extinct

the splendid Darwin's Finches of South America's Galapagos Islands and the amazingly diverse Hawaiian Honeycreepers whose members include seed and nectar eaters.

Undisturbed island species are often ridiculously tame. As Don Merton explains, "It's part of their undoing. Many of New Zealand's endemic birds have evolved through millions of years without encountering man or any other mammalian predators and competitors. New Zealand has no native land mammals other than bats – it split from the southern supercontinent called Gondwanaland some sixty-five million years ago – before the advent and dispersal of most mammals.

"Many of the birds have filled the roles or ecological niches that mammals exploit in other parts of the world. Kiwis, for example, with their long probing beaks and excellent sense of smell, are the feathered equivalents of small, insectivorous mammals like shrews and hedgehogs.

"Many of our birds are very tame and trusting, they can't fly (or can't fly well), they live a long time, they breed very, very slowly and have an incredibly low reproductive rate .... Biologists call this a 'K-selected' breeding strategy. What this translates into is this – at the individual level they are predator-naive, and at the population level, because they are slow breeders, they lack the ability to bounce back from adversity. These birds are terribly vulnerable. Their survival prospects in modern day New Zealand are compromised by a whole range of introduced predators and competitors we now have."

To illustrate just how destructive an alien predator can be, consider the case of the Stephen Island wren – the world's only flightless passerine (song bird). At the northern tip of New Zealand's South Island, about three kilometres from D'Urville Island in Cook Straits Marlborough Sounds, lies Stephen Island – a formerly wooded oasis some two and a half square kilometres in area. This island was the only known home of a unique species of wren, simultaneously discovered and wiped out in 1894.

During this period, the only inhabitant of Stephen Island was the lighthouse keeper, who was impressed by the 'ornithological finds' his cat kept bringing in. As the faithful feline continued to drop feathered presents at the feet of his master, the terrible truth dawned. One single, solitary lighthouse keeper's cat had managed to hunt an entire species to extinction.

Don Merton has spent all of his working life attempting to avert would-be lighthouse keeper cat situations. During more than three decades with the New Zealand Wildlife Service and Department of Conservation, he has pioneered many techniques for endangered species management. Today, New Zealand is a leader in the field and offers hope to many countries whose species and ecosystems have been disrupted and are at risk.

"When we started, there was a general lack of support at all levels," says Merton. "We had scant resources and folk had little appreciation of what we were trying to do. In those days, only two people worked full-time nationwide in this area. There's now at least forty people within the Department of Conservation with hands-on responsibility in this area. Public and political support is almost overwhelming."

One of the species to receive Don's attention was the black robin, an all black bird intermediate in size between a robin and a tit. The species was confined to low coastal 'akaeke' scrub on one offshore rock stack in the Chathams group, 850 km east of New Zealand.

When Don visited the Chathams in 1979, only five robins remained and only two of these were female – only one, however, proved to be an effective breeder. The species had to be saved from one pair – it was an incredibly long shot. The bird's breeding biology didn't help either. Black robins have a very slow reproductive rate for such a small bird. Normally two eggs are laid per year and the youngsters do not start breeding until they are two years old.

Everyone doubted the ability of the black robin to bounce back from apparent terminal adversity, but Don Merton had a hunch. He'd seen one nesting attempt fail and observed that the birds were giving it another go. Perhaps, just perhaps, he could take eggs from the robins and put them under another bird; cross foster them to a different species and thus induce the robins to lay more eggs – in fact twice as many as usual.

People had employed the technique with captive and domestic stock for centuries. This was different; there was no prospect of bringing the black robin into captivity. No specific trials had been done using mainland robins, only translocation trials, and unsuccessful attempts at keeping them in captivity. By taking eggs to encourage re-nesting and double or triple clutching (see chapter 7 *Return of the Big Birds?*), it was hoped to double or even treble the reproductive output of the robins.

This is Naturewatcher Don Merton with a juvenile female black robin. The black robin was one of the first species to receive Don's attention. When he first visited the Chathams, their natural home, only 5 robins remained, just one of which was a breeding female

To encourage the one black robin female to lay more eggs, eggs were taken away as they were laid, and these were fostered by Chatham Island tom tits. Here a tit (left) is feeding two black robin fledglings

Don's proposal was accepted by his superiors in the New Zealand Wildlife Service. In 1980 he returned to the Chathams to begin the most daring and innovative programme of his life. Each stage of the project involved the biological risk-taking equivalent of defusing a time-bomb.

First, the eggs had to be removed and the multiple clutching sequence set into motion. Second, foster parents had to be found. Don tried several species but finally settled for the Chatham Island tom tit which eagerly took up the challenge of hatching and rearing its disappearing neighbours. So far, so good. Until an unexpected variable cropped up.

The island where the work took place was considered pest-free – that is, no mammalian predators had been introduced there. But no one had taken into account another sort of danger – that from noisy, aggressive, introduced European starlings.

Millions of birds including tens of thousands of starlings found the island a safe haven, and this high density tended to inhibit the successful breeding of some, including the black robins. European starlings took it a stage further – in the competition for nest sites some would move in and destroy the nests, break the eggs and even kill the nestlings and the breeding females. Don Merton's response was to erect safe nest boxes in each black robin territory and for each tit foster-parent.

The tom tits continued to be great parents ... in fact they were too good. Just when Don Merton thought "we'd clinched it", some baby black robins had an identity crisis.

This is Old Blue, the sole original breeding black robin female, from which all black robins are descended. She lived for about 13 years, and was so famous that her death was announced in the New Zealand parliament.

Bird behaviour is part genetic, programmed (or innate) and part learnt from the parents at an early age. Several tit-raised robins were becoming imprinted on the tom tits and not behaving as they should. In extreme cases this inhibited them from breeding successfully with their own kind, presenting yet another hurdle for Don and his team to overcome.

The key was synchronisation of timing of hatching. Don decided to keep fostering but synchronised the hatching dates of near clutches of eggs. Just before the chicks fledged, he was then able to unite broods of similar age and return them as enlarged broods to the very few pairs of black robins for fledging.

It worked. Despite having three or four sets of parents, the new black robins were well adjusted behaviourally. Don kept a constant eye on their progress and had to support the parents with enlarged broods through supplementary feeding several times each day until the chicks were independent.

The story of the black robin caught the imagination of the New Zealand people. The sole original breeding female was dubbed 'Old Blue' after the colour of her leg-band and became a national celebrity. "It was fortuitous that she came along when she did," says Don Merton. "Without her there would be no black robins! It's hard to believe that there wasn't some divine intervention there somewhere."

Quite so. Old Blue lived for twice the lifespan of any other robin. Her productive years began when she was a geriatric nine years old (most robins are dead at about five or six years) and continued until her final season when she was about thirteen. Old Blue died in 1983/84 and her death was announced by the New Zealand parliament. Today, a decade later, Old Blue's genes live on in the one hundred and thirty-eight black robins that are her legacy. Old Blue is the only individual Don knows of that unquestionably has saved her species from certain extinction.

Don Merton is currently hoping to 'do a black robin' with another of New Zealand's unique and critically endangered birds, the kakapo or owl parrot.

"The kakapo really is a very special bird," he says. "It has a great many features that are unusual or unique. For instance, it's the heaviest of all parrots – about twice as heavy as the largest macaw. It's flightless, nocturnal and has a strange courtship system whereby males attract females by displaying for 3-4 months at traditional sites called leks. After mating males play no part in incubation and rearing of the young. The females are in fact single parents."

Kakapos have undergone a very marked decline in the last one hundred and fifty years. They became extinct on New Zealand's North Island early this century, and since the 1950s the only known animals on the mainland have all been males confined to the mountainous Fiordland region of the South Island. They are now extinct here too. Then, in 1977, the tide of kakapo history was turned when a small population was discovered in a remote corner of Stewart Island. Miraculously, the population contained some females, so hopes were rekindled for the survival of the species.

It was soon discovered, however, that feral domestic cats were well on the way to exterminating this last population. Consequently Don Merton and his colleagues began a programme of translocating the kakapos to offshore islands free

Don Merton and Zephyr, a 12 week old kakapo fledgling. The kakapo or owl parrot is one of New Zealand's most endangered birds

from alien predators and competitors. In 1982, he released twenty-two birds – nine females and thirteen males – onto Little Barrier Island. Eleven years later, most of them are still alive. Since then, twenty males and ten females have been relocated to Codfish Island near Stewart Island, and three males and three females to Maud Island in the Marlborough Sounds. Don considers these kakapos to be "biological refugees" – the last of their species.

During the last decade, the kakapo has become extinct on South Island. Stewart Island's long lost population is no more, decimated by the introduction of feral cats. The world kakapo population is about forty-five birds, of which only fifteen are females, marooned on three islands. As Don Merton says, "Since they cannot coexist with rats, cats and stoats, they have no hope of long term survival on the main islands of New Zealand."

The last chance for the curious owl parrot rests on the offshore islands. These are the only places where the birds can find refuge from alien animals. Kakapos don't congregate in large flocks like other parrots. They are solitary, except when on their lek, and as each has a home range of 30 to 50 hectares a viable population takes up a lot of room.

Don Merton believes that kakapos became seriously disadvantaged as soon as the introduced mammalian predators and competitors hit the New Zealand shores. "I believe they're uniquely vulnerable to predation," he says, and the evidence is, indeed, overwhelming. Kakapos have few defence strategies. They are green, a useful cryptic colour to blend in with Fiordland ferns and mosses and this undoubtedly was an effective defence against their historical enemies, giant eagles. However, this is no deterrent to a hungry stoat or cat that hunts by scent. Another trick to evade birds of prey is to freeze and crouch low. Added to this, kakapos have a strong, characteristic musty odour. So, although Kakapos with their nocturnal habit, cryptic colouration and ability to remain motionless were perfectly adapted to evade their only natural predators (birds of prey) they have no natural defences against mammalian predators that have now been introduced and which hunt by scent.

Don Merton is also interested in what kakapos eat. They are exclusively vegetarian and feed on a large variety of ferns, roots, leaves, fruit and tussock grasses. Considerable evidence is left everywhere they dine, although much of this can be confused with signs left by introduced possums. The most characteristic sign left by kakapo results from their habit of thoroughly chewing fibrous material and discarding the fibre in compact pellets or 'chews'.

Food availability is closely related to breeding performance. Kakapos do not normally breed every year, but the entire population breeds synchronously every four or five years when trees and grasses fruit or seed is particularly heavily. Don Merton decided to simulate and to increase the frequency of such 'bumper years' by supplementing the birds' feed on Little Barrier Island. This is not for the faint hearted. It involves long treks through very rugged country and it means climbing up and down over a couple of thousand feet a day. This technique has proved capable not only of inducing breeding, but also of greatly increasing the frequency of breeding attempts. It is therefore being employed on Codfish and Maud Islands too.

Don Merton provides food to supplement the kakapos' diets. This is not a job for the faint hearted as it involves long treks through rugged country like this at Tutoko Valley, Fiordland

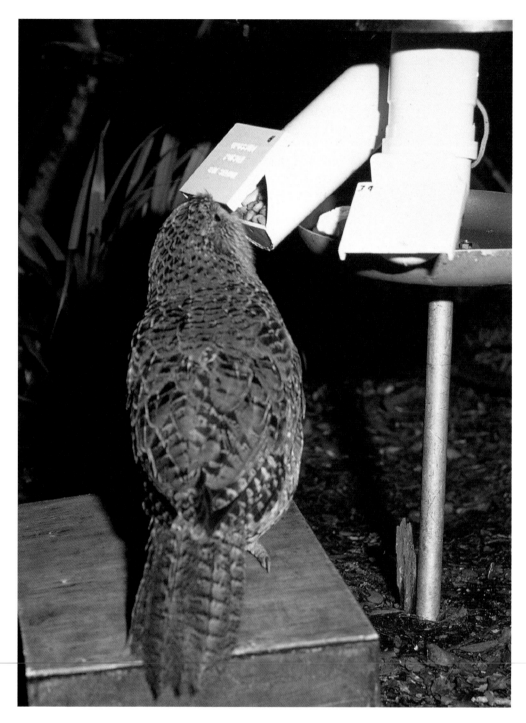

This is Heather, a female kakapo, taking food from the feeder put out by Don Merton. He supplements their natural diet of seeds and fruit to encourage breeding. To avoid rats stealing this food, the kakapo have to learn to open a flap in the feeder to gain access to the food

Kakapo tracks are maintained by the males on leks, year after year. Tracks elsewhere are not maintained by the birds. In order to find and catch birds, Don Merton puts out baits on wires that the birds start feeding from. Their favourite fare is apple and sweet potato, but these are also readily consumed by the introduced Polynesian rats on Little Barrier Island. So, once the kakapos are habituated to taking particular foods from particular tracks, Don constructs an intricate feeding station that resembles an award winning abstract sculpture. The birds soon learn to lift the kakapo equivalent of a cat flap to gain access to the food. The flap is effective in excluding rats.

Before the installation of the Don Merton all-purpose kakapo diners in 1989, the parrots had not shown signs of breeding for eight years. In 1990, only five months after feeding began, jubilant wildlife biologists found two nests, each containing an egg. One egg hatched but the chick did not survive. In 1991 four nests were found, and four eggs were airlifted by helicopter to Auckland Zoo, where keepers had been gaining experience with a similar species – another endangered endemic New Zealand parrot, the kaka.

Two of the eggs were infertile; the third contained an embryo which died before it reached the zoo. The final egg produced a chick. Despite a twenty-four hour vigil, the bird expired at five days of age. "Even with the setbacks, we have got further than ever before," said Richard Jakob-Hoff of Auckland Zoo.

A female kakapo feeds her ten week old chick. Although well adapted to evade their only natural predators, birds of prey, kakapos have no natural defences against introduced mammalian predators and were at risk of extinction until interventionary management by Don Merton rescued them

Back on Little Barrier Island, the chick's mother (christened 'John Girl') and one other female each raised one healthy nestling. In 1992 at least five females on Codfish Island nested, but the natural food supply failed and since the kakapo were not having their food supplemented, most of the nestlings starved to death. However, three were rescued and one of these was hand-raised by Auckland Zoo and is now in captivity on Maud Island – the first of a captive population that is to be established as an ultimate safety-net for the species. In 1993 booming (lek display) and mating occurred on all three islands but only two nests were found (on Little Barrier Island). Only one chick is known to have hatched but this was apparently eaten by rats within a few days of hatching. The reason for the poor breeding performance can probably be attributed to 'El Nino' climatic conditions and an experimental reduction in the supplemental diets during the past two winters – a time when food seems in greatest demand. Diets have since been increased, and rat control measures at nests are to be intensified in the future. Don Merton is optimistic that the kakapo will join a growing list of New Zealand birds rescued by interventionary management in the wild; birds like the takahe, a flightless rail, the saddleback, an endemic wattle bird species (this was saved by Don and was his first major success), the black robin and New Zealand's most famous bird, the kiwi. The New Zealand Department of Conservation is presently busy translocating populations of the smallest and most endangered of the three kiwi species, the little spotted, to offshore islands.

Putting birds back is only part of the philosophy behind New Zealand's conservation policies. Securing, protecting and restoring the habitat and reinstating natural systems are the ultimate goals. This will be impossible for some species; half of the ninety-six endemic species of land birds that existed until people started to settle on the islands one thousand years ago are now extinct. This includes the eleven species of moa; huge flightless birds that exceeded the ostrich in size, and the largest eagle ever known that fed on the moas. Almost half of the unique native frogs have gone, and it is impossible to estimate how many reptile and invertebrate species have been lost.

But New Zealand is better off than many countries because humans settled there so comparatively recently. There are around seven hundred offshore islands, many of them safe or potentially safe havens for native and in particular endangered species. The restoration ecologists have to first clear such islands of damaging rodent pests. It can be done. Many islands have already been cleared of rats and many other alien animal species.

Each island is assessed on its own merits. A comprehensive plan, appropriate to the island, is worked out and a sequence of events agreed upon. After the rodents and any other alien animals are eradicated, selected indigenous plants and animals are returned to the islands and the associated recovery of communities of plants and invertebrates, seabirds and reptiles is carefully monitored and where necessary managed.

Don Merton sees his work as 'firefighting'. Big changes, he thinks, will only continue to happen if New Zealand's younger generation care about their country's natural heritage. When Don began his pioneering work in the early 1960s only he and one other were involved nationwide. Now about 40 people within New Zealand's

Department of Conservation have responsibility for and are actively involved in management of threatened species. Don is optimistic about the future; especially in the light of media interest about conservation and TV programmes like *Nature Watch* which are taking his achievements to a global audience and so inspiring others to take up the challenge in the midst of the current global species crisis.

Nature Watch has also been instrumental in publicising the work of Carl Jones, a young Welsh ornithologist responsible for captive breeding and reintroduction of endangered endemic birds to Mauritius. Carl is a friend of Don Merton's, and Don has visited Maritius several times to help with the work there, rehabilitating small offshore islands and helping with the rare endemic birds.

The tropical paradise island of Mauritius lies eight hundred kilometres east of Madagascar in the Indian Ocean. Largest of the Mascarene islands (the others are Rodriguez and Réunion), Mauritius comprises over two thousand square kilometres of coastal lowland and central plains surrounded by mountains. The island is volcanic in origin and encircled with coral reefs. The dodo used to live in Mauritius. Early

The extinction of the famous dodo on Mauritius was brought about entirely by human intervention: they were slaughtered for food, their habitat destroyed, and their eggs and chicks fell prey to introduced mammals. Naturewatcher Carl Jones is trying to prevent the same fate befalling other Mauritian birds

Carl Jones (here with 3 Mauritius kestrel chicks) is a Welsh ornithologist responsible for the captive breeding and reintroduction of endangered endemic birds to Mauritius

colonists (the island was discovered by Portuguese navigators in the sixteenth century) reported several species of turkey-sized flightless pigeons. One of these was the dodo – a unique bird with strong legs and feet to root for grubs and shoots in the Mauritian forest. Its trusting, harmless demeanour was to lead to its downfall.

Portuguese and Dutch sailors, hungry for fresh meat, found the slow-moving dodo an easy target. They also chopped down its forest habitat and released rats, cats, dogs, pigs and monkeys onto Mauritius. Like New Zealand, Mauritius was formerly without native land mammals other than bats.

The combined effects of slaughter for food, habitat loss and the predation of chicks and eggs resulted in the dodo's demise some one hundred and eighty-six years after it was first seen by Europeans. The phrase 'dead as a dodo' has passed into the language as a euphemism for extinction everywhere.

Carl Jones arrived in Mauritius in 1979, over three hundred years after the dodo disappeared. The thirty or forty species of bird reported by European sailors centuries earlier had dwindled to eleven indigenous types, including the world's rarest pigeon, falcon and parrot. Carl is Conservation Field Officer of the Jersey Wildlife Preservation Trust who, with the encouragement of the Mauritian government, has spearheaded a campaign to rescue the latterday would-be dodos. His base, the government aviaries of Black River, is crammed with rare endemic birds and an eccentric collection of exotic house guests that includes monkeys and Rupert, a hedgehog-like nocturnal insectivorous mammal called a tenrec.

Carl's first love was, and is, birds of prey. He says, "I worship them. My parents tell me that I've always had a deep love of birds of prey. Or as Konrad Lorenz would say, I've become imprinted upon them. Just as they imprint upon me, I've imprinted upon them, and it's a wonderful relationship."

Carl's message is that you have to be able to empathise with birds of prey to really understand them. "The only way we can really understand animals is to be involved with them and identify with their emotions" he says. "I know when my falcons are angry. I know their motivational states because I've lived with them. When I first started keeping birds of prey and owls, I found it difficult to understand them. But by living with them twenty-four hours a day, keeping them in my bedroom at night, they've become an extension of me. It's not something you can put down on paper – a lot of it is subconscious."

One bird of prey – the Mauritius kestrel – owes its continued survival to Carl Jones. In the 1970s this petite forest falcon was considered the world's rarest bird; in 1974 only four individuals were known to remain in the wild. How did it get into such a precarious position? Carl Jones explains:

"You've only got to look at the island and you'll see that it has been vastly altered: there's sugar cane fields over sixty per cent of Mauritius; a lot of the native vegetation has been chopped down, and one of the worst causes of the decline has been the introduction of alien species by the early colonisers."

Mauritius kestrels nest on rocky cliffs and gorges that are also frequented by predatory rats and monkeys. Carl has seen monkeys within metres of a nest and, in the early days, heard stories of one hundred per cent predation by monkeys climbing up the cliffs to take the eggs and young.

Many island birds fail to adapt to changing circumstances. As in New Zealand, native animals tended to be relatively slow breeders, and could not bounce back from adversity without help. As a forest species, the Mauritius kestrel has had more than its fair share of habitat change to contend with.

"First of all, if you cut down the forests, you're going to lose all the birds in the forest," says Carl. "But here the very nature of the forest has altered. Early sailors talked about a forest rich in ebony and tropical hardwoods. There were four layers and an open canopy, and the kestrels evolved a flying and hunting strategy to fit in with the environment."

The ecology of the Mauritius kestrel depends upon their main prey, the beautiful bright green day geckos known as phelsumas. The phelsumas depend upon the native

The Mauritius kestrel owes its survival to Carl Jones. Considered the world's rarest bird in 1970, Carl has successfully bred this species in captivity and since 1984 has reintroduced captive bred birds to sites all over Mauritius

This is a phelsuma, the main prey of the Mauritius kestrel. As the forests were cut down so these geckos suffered and this was in turn reducing kestrel populations

vegetation. As the indigenous forest is cut down or destroyed by cyclones, introduced alien flora takes over. It now seems clear that the main reason for the very low number of birds was pesticide contamination. The island was sprayed with DDT to kill malaria-carrying mosquitoes.

Carl Jones has been captive breeding Mauritius kestrels for over ten years now. The breeding first began in 1973, but in 1979 all the captive kestrels died. Analysis revealed that they harboured high pesticide levels in their bodies, and that their eggs showed classic signs of pesticide thinning. When Carl resumed the programme in 1981, expectations were low.

The Welshman was undeterred. He had seen a wild pair lay eggs and decided to embark upon a two hundred metre haul up low cliffs strewn with creepers, vines and loose rocks. The three eggs were examined – any cracks could be sealed with nail varnish – and carefully packed in cotton wool inside a thermos flask to maintain the incubation temperature. They were then transported back to the Black River aviaries, weighed, measured and numbered before being placed in an incubator. Carl Jones stayed with them around the clock. His worst fear was a power cut – but at least there were emergency generators.

Three weeks later, after forty hours of heaving and pushing accompanied by incessant 'chupping' sounds, the first chick hatched, followed by another. The third egg was infertile. Thus began a continuous programme of egg collection and manipulation of wild kestrels to produce multiple clutches.

The baby kestrels were easy enough to rear. After all, Carl had a successful record of hand raising birds of prey. He fed them on mice. "For the first few days I give them the internal organs. Then I skin the mice and feed the kestrels little bits of minced mouse every four hours to start with. You have to make sure that they're kept at the right temperature, and later on that they're brought up with other siblings or else you'll get imprinting problems. We've got to make sure that they grow up as balanced, well adjusted kestrels."

Since 1984 juvenile captive-bred kestrels have been returned to sites all over Mauritius. Carl has become an expert at surreptitiously adding 'his' babies to the nests of unsuspecting wild adults whilst simultaneously removing their eggs. Resurrecting his old falconry 'hacking' skills, Carl also takes well developed captive bred birds back into the forest, provides them with nest boxes and supplementary feeding, and allows them to fledge on their own. By the beginning of 1992, the two hundredth captive bred kestrel had been released into the wild. The latest estimate of the free ranging population is 220-240 birds which includes fifty to fifty-five breeding pairs.

Another Carl Jones speciality is a spectacular pigeon that, like its famous extinct relative the dodo, is the largest Mauritian land bird.

This pigeon is pink and lives in forests where it feeds upon the leaves, flowers and fruits of native trees. Every November to March, the pink pigeon nests in tree branches and, after mating, females lay one or two pure white eggs. Out of these hatch blind, almost featherless chicks that are fed by mum and dad on regurgitated 'crop milk', a protein and fat-packed secretion from the crop lining.

Early settlers to Mauritius found pink pigeon meat to be unpalatable and poisonous. Perhaps that is why the species has survived to this day, despite running the usual gamut of Mauritian menaces like the ever-present egg predating primates and rats and delayed breeding seasons resulting from unseasonal weather.

Carl Jones has bred lots of pink pigeons in aviaries, but, in the early days it nearly drove him mad. "Pink pigeons are the worst parents you could ever imagine. If you want to give anyone a nervous breakdown, give them some pink pigeons to look after," he says. "Pigeons are supposed to be easy to breed but these hate each other and beat each other up. If they get to the nest building stage, you're lucky. But then they lay their eggs off perches, lay infertile eggs, smash and trample eggs. Even if, by some fluke, the female lays a fertile egg the chances are the parents won't look after it properly."

At first, Carl solved the problem by incubating pink pigeon eggs under doves who proved model parents. Later, after much trial and error, and the mixing and matching of different pigeons with each other, compatible pairs were established and successful breeding ensued. Today over two hundred and twenty pink pigeons are held in Mauritius and collections in Jersey, Europe and the United States.

When the captive population reached secure levels in 1984, the first phase of a reintroduction programme was initiated. Twenty-two captive bred adults were released into the Royal Botanic Gardens at Pamplemousses. However, many of these were killed by marauding monkeys and small boys with catapults. Others were recaptured by Carl.

Subsequent reintroductions have been more successful, and today pink pigeons fly free in the upland forest of Macchabe/Brisefer, an area from where they were absent for over a decade. There are still only some twenty-five truly wild pink pigeons, but their numbers have been swelled by twenty-five established released birds.

The pink pigeon is the largest Mauritian land bird. Carl Jones breeds this species but has to incubate the pigeon eggs under doves as the pigeons make very poor parents. Pink pigeons have been reintroduced successfully to at least one area from where they had become extinct

Now Carl Jones' attentions have turned to the world's rarest parrot, the echo parakeet. About twenty-two remain wild in Black River gorge, threatened by habitat loss, alien predators and competition with introduced ring-necked parakeets. Eggs have been harvested from the wild and reared in captivity. There are now three birds surviving in the Black River Aviaries.

The conservation battle for this species has just begun. It will also, doubtless, soon begin for other unique island birds across the planet. Many critics of the manipulative management techniques pioneered by people like Don Merton and Carl Jones have been silenced. For Don and Carl have each demonstrated that interventionary management of a critically-endangered species living in the wild can be highly effective, and even in the most extreme circumstance – *four* Mauritius kestrels or just *one* remaining pair of Black robins – recovery is possible!

This is the majestic white or Arabian oryx - thought to be the basis of the unicorn myth. Ancient practise involved the binding of the horns of young oryx together causing them to fuse as they grow and produce a one-horned animal

CHAPTER SIX
ORYX GO HOME

The large hoofed mammal stood motionless and surveyed its sandy environment. Convinced that there was no imminent danger, it proceeded cautiously up to the summit of a nearby dune and froze at ninety degrees to the desert moon. In silhouette, only one horn, slender and curved, was visible. It might have been a unicorn.

Crouched low, under the cover of a thorny shrub, an Arab from the nomadic Bedu tribe of Harasis put down his binoculars and spoke into a two-way radio. He did not intend to harm the animal; merely to report on its whereabouts to English zoologist and Naturewatcher, Mark Stanley-Price.

This unicorn was no mythical beast. In some areas, people called it 'baqr al washah' or wild cow. The ancient Hebrew word for unicorn – 'Reem' – is also translated as 'wild ox' in all modern versions of the bible. But, although a member of the cattle family – indeed the largest Arabian member of the cattle family – this animal, majestic in profile, was a white or Arabian oryx.

Dr Mark Stanley-Price and his wife Karen first became intimately involved with the Arabian oryx in the early 1980s. The species had already been extinct in the wild for almost a decade when the Stanley-Prices landed in Oman to take up the challenge of re-

Animals are not abundant in the desert. Scorpions spend their days dug deep into the sand, coming out in the cool of the night to feed

introducing zoo-bred oryx to the wild. Mark was uniquely qualified to manage the project as he had previously studied a related species, the Beisa oryx, under captive and field conditions in East Africa. Conditions in Oman, though, were to prove much harsher.

The Jidda' desert is one of the most inhospitable places on Earth. It is a stony desert with very little surface sand. To the north and west lies Arabia's Rub'al-Khal, or empty quarter, an area the size of France that contains the world's largest continuous body of sand. To the east is the Hufq escarpment. A narrow coastal plain separates the Jidda' from the Indian Ocean.

Mark Stanley-Price designated an area of the Jidda' as the oryx reintroduction site. It comprises 25,000 square kilometres of, by desert standards, well developed vegetation which is gradually replaced by relatively barren desert to the west. The region is as big – and as unknown – as Albania.

As one might expect, the place is abnormally dry and hot. There is no natural permanent source of water and the rainfall is so erratic – it once came in bouts six years apart – that calculating averages means little. Most of the desert animals have adapted their physiology to conserve water. They obtain moisture from plants and void very concentrated urine, for example. Some occasionally drink from brackish water seepages and there are hand dug wells at the foot of the Hufq escarpment.

When *Nature Watch* filmed in the Jidda', the temperature was thirty-nine degrees Celsius (about one hundred degrees Fahrenheit) in the shade. "This is what I call spring weather," said Mark Stanley-Price. "Come in another month's time and the monthly average will be between forty-four and forty-eight degrees Celsius in the shade. Heaven knows how much that makes it in the sun."

Despite the discomfort, Mark Stanley-Price has grown to love the desert. "I think it has great visual beauty," he says. "Admittedly it does depend on the time of day. The sand dunes look absolutely beautiful in the low light of early morning or evening. The more you live here, the more you realise that the place is not uniform. You become very sensitive to very small changes in the landscape and the pattern of plant communities."

Animals are not overabundant in the desert, but with patience, experience and a keen eye, the dedicated desert watcher becomes privy to a rich complement of fauna. "Don't expect to see herds and herds of, say, large antelope," says Mark. "Here you appreciate the geckos, the beetles, the little things as well as the bigger species. There are different types of desert and various microhabitats within each type. Each one has its own special animals. The water holes attract insects and birds that need water. Out here, in this much drier, sandy desert, you have more forms that can run over the sand surface or burrow into it. Scorpions spend their days dug deep into the soft sand, coming out at night to feed."

A zoologist can find interest and excitement in any environment. For Mark Stanley-Price, though, the stories of man's exploration of and adaptation to desert life were as fascinating as the habitat's biology. As he says, "For the early English explorers the great appeal of this place was in the local people who respond to the hard life in the same way as the animals. They're all up against it, they all have to get on. Everyone's meeting the same demands and I think that the society and way of life around here has adapted to do just that. I think that appeals very much."

The local people are the Harasis tribe of nomadic Bedu. Historically, they lived in harmony with the environment and had a benevolent attitude towards their wildlife. They were not responsible for the former plight of the oryx.

"The Harasis protected the oryx as their own resource," says Mark Stanley-Price. "Undoubtedly, they shot the larger antelopes and the smaller ones like gazelle because any source of meat was not to be sneezed at. But if you talk to any Harasis hunters of that period, they'll tell you that they never, ever took more than one animal at a time."

Would that they could. In the vast open tracts of the Jidda', an oryx with its fantastic eyesight would be an extremely difficult animal to surprise. The Bedu had to employ a variety of tricks to get close.

Most desert animals such as these camels have adapted their physiology to conserve water. They obtain moisture from plants and void very concentrated urine

"The hunters went out looking for oryx footprints," says Mark. "Upon finding them, they'd scout around the area until they saw the herd. Then it was a matter of dismounting their camels, actually taking off all the saddlery and equipment, hiding that under a bush and then making the camel walk towards the oryx as though it was a free ranging animal. The hunter used the camel as cover. He'd hide behind a particular leg and only move when the leg moved. There was a rule of thumb that when you could see the white sock between the black hoof and the black of the leg with the naked eye, you were close enough to risk a shot. I can't imagine that the success rate was very high and, anyway, for many years the number of oryx in the area was very low."

The decline of the Arabian oryx began during the Second World War and was accelerated by the invention of the jeep and four-wheel-drive vehicles. Much better weapons were suddenly available and motorised hunting took over, often with submachine guns. It was a far cry from the Bedu's muzzle loading rifles and bows and arrows. By 1960, the wild population was reduced to between one and two hundred animals in the deserts of southern Arabia. In the same year, a specially equipped motor caravan carried members of Qatari's ruling tribe across eight hundred kilometres of open desert to kill twenty-eight oryx – a major portion of the two remaining large herds of the time.

The indiscriminate slaughter of the oryx was unnatural and incomprehensible to the Bedu. They had always followed their own rules of living equitably within nature.

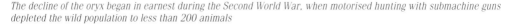

The decline of the oryx began in earnest during the Second World War, when motorised hunting with submachine guns depleted the wild population to less than 200 animals

When they killed an oryx, nothing went to waste. The meat was prized and used for exorcising demons. The intestines functioned as containers for the fat, blood and water that served as treatments for snake bite. In addition, fat was rubbed or burnt and inhaled as an alleged cure for rheumatism. Juices from oryx stomachs extended the Bedu's sparse water supply, and any half digested gut contents could be fed to the camels. Rifle butts were fashioned from the fine leather, and the renowned horns were carved into plaintive pipes for Arab shepherd boys.

Oryx hunting was a highly skilled artform as practised by the Bedu. It was often dangerous, and young tribesmen killed their first oryx to prove their manhood. One story has it that a particular Arab went to track down his brother after the latter failed to return to the tribal camp following an oryx hunt. The man was found bleeding to death on the antelope's back, a horn impaled through his thigh. Afraid to shoot in case he hit his brother, the Arab tossed him a knife. The hunter then freed himself and killed the unfortunate animal.

The motorcades continued to massacre the white oryx. Soon, Oman was the last place left with a viable population. The Arab hunters had now been joined by expatriate oilmen from the foreign oil companies. Wasting a few oryx was just another way of livening up what was, to them, a desolate and desperate existence in the desert.

"Central Oman was very undeveloped in the mid-1960s," says Mark Stanley-Price. "Large hunting parties were coming in from across the borders which were barely marked, let alone protected. Huge numbers of gazelle and oryx were shot, and in the face of that, the Harasis, who didn't even have cars, couldn't do a thing. They had to stand by and witness the slaughter of the last herds here."

In 1974, His Majesty Sultan Caboose banned all hunting and falconry in Oman. From that day on the number of gazelles shot has been very slight. It was too late for the oryx, though. The last wild herd was exterminated in 1972.

The species was not entirely extinct, however. During the carnage of the 1960s and early 1970s, another story had been slowly unfurling. It is a story of conservation through captive breeding and reintroduction. A story that features Mark Stanley-Price in the second and final acts as the leading character and hero of the piece. The story starts back in Britain.

In 1961, reports reached the United Kingdom that poachers had attacked what was probably the last wild population of Arabian oryx. This was the Qatari episode previously mentioned. The Fauna and Flora Preservation Society (FFPS) and World Conservation Union (IUCN) decided to mount an expedition to capture some of the surviving oryx with the aim of breeding them in captivity and, at a future date, reintroducing them to the wild. Major Ian Grimwood, then Kenya's Chief Game Warden, was headhunted as team leader. Operation Oryx was thus born.

The expedition moved into the desert in April 1962. At its helm was a customised capture car, and Piper Cub for aerial scouting. Together with the tents and bearers, some morale boosting alcohol had been smuggled in along with the help of the British Army. Grimwood's men moved fast as fresh reports of poaching had come to light.

It was across 10 000 square kilometres of this inhospitable terrain that the first expedition set out in 1962 to capture the last remaining wild Arabian oryx

After fruitlessly searching over ten thousand square kilometres of sandy terrain, the Arab tracker Tomatum (so called because his father loved tomatoes) came across some old oryx tracks. At least the species was still alive. Eventually, some mornings later, fresh droppings were found. The party moved slowly; their quarry would be seeking shade. Just before 10.00 a.m. an oryx belted from behind a bush some two hundred metres in the distance. The capture truck was set instantly into motion. After two or three abortive capture attempts, the oryx was finally noosed. It was a male. Subsequent forays into the desert yielded two more animals, another male and a female. Christened Pat, Edith and (in honour of the man who found it) Tomatum, the Omani three were flown out of the Middle East, where no suitable areas remained for their release.

The antelope were taken to one of America's greatest zoos in Phoenix, Arizona; a location selected for its climactic similarity to Arabia. There they were joined by a lone female from London Zoo and other animals donated by the Kuwaiti and Saudi royal families. Nine oryx now lived in captivity – the nucleus of a World Herd.

Fortunately the species bred well in captivity. The first calf was produced in October 1963, although the first female calf did not appear until September 1966. Meanwhile, throughout the 1960s, another member of the Qatari ruling family undertook several expeditions to southern Arabia to capture oryx for breeding. Apparently he once assured an anxious engineer that each animal was personally transported in the back of its own Cadillac! Additionally, during the same period, other individuals were involved in captive breeding on the Arabian peninsula.

By the 1970s, the world herd had increased to thirty-four animals. These were dispersed among several zoos as an insurance policy lest an epidemic wipe out the species. Zoos receiving oryx agreed to supply any animals needed for reintroduction into the wild. When news broke that the last oryx had been shot in the wild, Operation Oryx was finally justified, although the operation itself may have stimulated further efforts to capture wild oryx for captive breeding on the Arabian peninsula.

In 1978, four captive oryx were released into enclosures within the Shaumari Wildlife Reserve in Jordan. The Jordanian government established the reserve to conserve a representative portion of habitat known as the 'Eastern Desert Land Type', an extensive wadi system containing rich plant and animal communities. Oryx breeding at Shaumari has been successful, as it also has in neighbouring Israel where a herd of the desert antelope live within a fenced reserve at Hai Bar South in the Negev desert.

In 1980, Operation Oryx received a major breakthrough. The Sultan of Oman took a personal interest and plans were made to release oryx into the wild. Enter the Stanley-Prices.

Naturewatcher Dr Mark Stanley-Price came to Oman with his wife Karen with the challenge of re-introducing zoo-bred oryx into the wild where they had been extinct for almost ten years

A complete village was built at Wadi Yalooni, with its own generating plant, airstrip and workshops. Work commenced on an enormous acclimatisation enclosure for the oryx. Mark Stanley-Price set off to recruit co-workers and got to know the Harasis.

"A lot of my work consisted of tracking animals, usually every morning," says Mark. "It was necessary to recognise individual animals and the Harasis do this without effort. Following oryx in a stony desert like the Jidda' requires very special skills. The Harasis learnt these skills as boys, and I don't think anyone else in the world could do the job. Their local knowledge is so great that all the patches of vegetation have their own names. Often single trees of characteristic shape, where perhaps an old man once lived, are named."

Mark has known Harasis rangers in different patrols to have a short radio conversation and then meet at a precise tree in about 100,000 square kilometres. He works very closely with them to monitor the oryx's progress. "For the project to be a success, we have to work with the co-operation and enthusiasm of the local people. We can't force them to be here or not to be here, to do this or do that. They have to be convinced it's in their interest or in the interests of the project and hence their long term employment prospects."

In 1981, the first batch of five zoo-bred oryx, descendants of the original nine, were flown back to the Sultanate of Oman, and then, in sky vans of the Sultan's Air Force to Yalooni. Mark was understandably nervous. Any reintroduction programme implies controlled risk taking and a feasibility study had been undertaken of the release site. But could the animals cope?

No one expected the oryx to step out of a plane's cargo hold and wander straight into the desert. First they had to be acclimatised to the harsh terrain. The animals had been shepherded into crates in America, their long horns encased in rubber tubing for protection. They had endured a stressful ninety hour flight. They needed to settle down.

"We opened the crates and let the animals into holding pens," says Mark Stanley-Price. "They've got to get used to seeing people wearing, to them at least, rather funny clothes, and making very different noises. The sights and sounds are all different, so we leave them in the pens in small groups. As long as we get the combination of sex and age right, they won't fight."

The holding pens lead into a one square kilometre enclosure fenced with two metre high chainlink and strategically sited for its abundance of local vegetation types. It is here where the development of an integrated herd takes place.

Wild oryx normally live in groups of ten to twenty animals, although aggregations of up to one hundred individuals have been recorded. Groups consist of both sexes and are often led by an older female. Within an integrated herd there is a dominance hierarchy involving all animals over six months of age. Herd structure is cohesive, and when the oryx are together, the overall interaction level is low. This ensures that the animals know each other and want to be with each other. Thus, they are less likely to scatter upon final release to the wild. Integration takes place about six months after the addition of the last new oryx.

Oryx overcome the fierce desert heat by seeking out the shade of any trees they can find during the day

Enclosed oryx are easy to observe. Mark Stanley-Price will not even think of liberating his charges until he has seen a full expected complement of social and sexual behaviour. Dominant males, for example, mark their home ranges by squatting and producing conspicuous pyramids of faeces. During the first ever acclimatisation, one male acquired dominance when two years of age. He did not, however, start depositing the dung until eighteen months later when two new males joined his pen. Only then did he have the social skills and maturity to keep a herd together in the desert.

Then there is the problem of heat and water to surmount. Oryx have a head start - their adaptations and physiology are well suited to cope with life in what must seem like a furnace. The white coat reflects much of the sun's radiation during the heat of the desert day. In the cold winter the coat grows thicker which also helps the oryx retain body heat at night. Temperature regulation is achieved in addition by behaviour. Oryx seek out the shade of small shrub-like trees during the day and then make shallow scrapes with their front hooves so that they lie in cooler sand and reduce the

Wild oryx get all the moisture they need from eating plants and licking the morning dew from plants

surface area exposed to drying winds (excess water loss must also be avoided). As Mark Stanley-Price puts it: they are experts at 'fine-tuning' heat regulation. They seek shade earlier on hot days, and they do not move out again until a cooler evening breeze blows.

There still remains the challenge of taking a herd that has been used to regular food and water, and releasing them into an area where it might not rain for six years. Mark Stanley-Price explains:

"Basically we let the animals take it at their own pace. We did this with the first herd. When it rained there was obviously standing water they could drink ad lib. As that dried up it was obvious they wanted water again and we provided it for them in a trough. As they moved further away, they knew the only water was at Yalooni. Therefore they had to calculate the benefits of having a drink against the cost of walking in to get it ... and it was entirely dependent on the temperature. On very hot periods they'd walk in every two days for a drink. As it cooled, the interval spread to three, four or five days. Then, at the end of their first summer, they detected an area of good grazing 25 kilometres from Yalooni. It was in early September, the temperatures were dropping, the grass was green. They walked in from there once, taking two and a half days to get here and back, and they never did it again."

The oryx had done their sums. By shading a bit more and feeding on the greenery at night, they would get more water with less effort than by hitting the trail to Yalooni. Like truly wild oryx they can now live indefinitely without open water. They receive enough moisture from eating plants, licking morning dew, and from the occasional foggy spell. Only because of the heavy fogs that roll in from the Indian Ocean at night do the grasses and shrubs that the oryx need for grazing stay edible and nourishing. The overnight condensation provides just enough water for them to survive.

When the enclosure gates were finally opened, neither the oryx nor the observers knew what lay over the horizon. One of the first things the animals did was to explore what they'd already seen. Then one individual, usually a senior female, would decide to move somewhere else. She started walking off and, if nobody else followed, stopped, and without moving her body, looked over her shoulder at the rest. Oryx continually watch each other, and the female's stance was an invitation to the others to get moving.

The Arabian oryx has black and white patterns over its face and legs. Noted artist and zoologist Jonathan Kingdon says that the markings make the animals extremely conspicuous every time they move or adopt certain postures. This is useful if you live within a social system and need to communicate feelings, wants and needs to co-specifics. Markings also enable oryx to maintain contact. These animals wander off by themselves for days at a time, apparently following well-worn trails hidden in the sand or the deep recesses of their brains. Following tracks is one way of staying in touch. Another strategy is to stand immobile on the crest of a sand dune in the hope of being noticed. It works, although historically it also had the devastating effect of shouting to hunters, "Here I am, shoot me".

Mark Stanley-Price reintroduced two Arabian oryx herds to the wild. He was helped by the Harasis guardians, and by the dominant oryx bulls who prevented their charges from wandering too far until they were conversant with the pitfalls of desert life. Gradually, the antelope learnt about their new environment. "I've seen them return to an area after several months absence," says Mark, "and go precisely to where they know the bones of a dead camel will be lying. They chew those presumably to get minerals."

Experience with the oryx helped Mark Stanley-Price to set up a Reintroduction Group of the World Conservation Union. Today, there are over one hundred reintroduction projects worldwide. It will never replace habitat preservation as the main thrust of wildlife conservation, but it is an increasingly popular tool of environmental management. Because of reintroduction, species like the red wolf roam wild again in North America, the Bali mynah in Indonesia and Przewalski's horse in central Asia.

The Arabian oryx reintroduction probably proved successful because the desert is a relatively 'simple' environment compared to, say, the three dimensional complexity

of a rainforest (although rainforest reintroductions have been successful too – witness the return of the golden lion tamarin monkey to Brazil's Atlantic coastal forests). The oryx had no natural predators and its demise was not due to habitat destruction. The 'wild' still existed, and once the threats – i.e. the hunters – were removed, the stage was set for a safe release programme.

When Mark Stanley-Price returned to the Jidda' in 1990, there were over one hundred oryx living free. Grazing was good as the desert had received regular rain since 1987. Detailed monitoring by the ever present Harasis wardens showed that over half the population is under three years of age. Over the past few years, good local conditions have resulted in a first year calf survival rate of ninety per cent. Elsewhere, acclimatised oryx have been liberated into the two thousand seven hundred square kilometre fenced Mahazet as Sayed reserve in Saudi Arabia.

"It's almost certain that the white oryx was the basis for the unicorn myth," says Mark Stanley-Price. "Aristotle, in his *Historia Animalium*, refers to the practice in Ancient Egypt of binding the horns of young oryx together when they're growing. At that stage they're not firmly attached to the skull, so you can manipulate them and change the shape. So if you bind the two horns together they will grow and actually fuse, producing a genuinely one-horned animal."

Thus, as well as saving an important part of Arabia's heritage, Mark Stanley-Price has saved an animal that is special for all of us. A creature fixed in our folklore, legends and dreams.

Today, as Mark says, "another dream has come true. Once again, hundreds of priceless white unicorns are roaming all over the desert."

Guards keep a very close eye on the re-introduced oryx. Thanks to their efforts and those of the Stanley-Prices, wild oryx again roam free across the Jidda' desert

The Californian condor is the biggest vulture, with a wingspan of over 3 metres

CHAPTER SEVEN
RETURN OF THE BIG BIRDS?

Who's the biggest vulture in California? Ask a number of sunshine state denizens and you'd probably get a variety of replies ranging from the LA Police department to the fearsome looking gang that lives on the block down the road.

All would be wrong. The biggest buzzard (that's what Americans call vultures) is the Californian condor, a bird of prey of giant proportions; the wingspan is over three metres (about half the height of a giraffe) across and the scales are tipped at a record breaking 11 kilograms.

Unfortunately, the Californian condor no longer graces the West Coast skies with its daunting silhouette. Its decline and fall illustrates many of the conundrums of modern conservation biology.

Naturewatcher Noel Snyder has headed a last ditch attempt to understand and halt the extinction of this magnificent bird. He's in charge of the Condor Recovery Programme and Condor Research Team which was set up in 1980 with grants totalling $1 million from the US Fish and Wildlife Service and the National Audubon Society.

Californian condors have been around a long time. They are relicts of an age when California was a lot cooler. In fact the species is a leftover of the Pleistocene or Ice Ages that geologists believe ended about 10,000 years ago. At that time the vast

vultures soared above giant ground sloths, sabre toothed tigers and majestic woolly mammoths. Noel Snyder says that the bird was formerly found all the way up to southern Canada along the Pacific coast into southern British Columbia. It used to occur, even into the 1930s, in Baja California in Mexico.

By the time Europeans settled in North America, Californian condors were restricted to the western states. Since the 1940s, when there were about 60-100 birds living wild, the population has undergone a steady decline.

"I don't think there's a single factor responsible for the deaths," says Snyder. "If I were to make a guess, and that's all it would be, I think shooting may be the most important factor. Either that or the secondary effect of shooting. The birds often feed on carcasses pockmarked with bullets and succumb to lead poisoning. We had a case of it a year ago. It only took a tiny fragment of a lead bullet to cause the death of a bird. But it's the only case we've had where we could prove the cause of death."

Perhaps the big birds just can't handle having people in close proximity. After all, the decline has been pretty consistent ever since people appeared on the North American continent. Snyder doesn't agree.

"The bird seems pretty tolerant of man. I think you have to look at the other side of the coin. It's man and what he does to the bird rather than the bird's reaction to man. The birds are actually exposed to human disturbance on a daily basis, so they're used to it. I mean, they yawn when aeroplanes fly over. Probably their problems lie more in the fact that they aren't concerned enough about people. They're very easily approached ... and shot."

Naturewatcher Noel Snyder, here talking with Julian Pettifer, is in charge of the Condor Recovery Programme and Condor Research Team, who are trying to halt the extinction of this magnificent bird

Another major cause of mortality was consuming poisoned carcasses left out by farmers as bait for the marauding coyotes that prey on their livestock. Pesticide residues found in the tissues of postmortemed birds have also been very high, and eggshells have had up to 50 per cent thinning compared with eggs laid before the widespread usage of organochlorines.

As the big birds tumbled ever on into extinction, conservationists raged fierce battles over how to save them. Interventionists, led by Noel Snyder, wanted to bring

This bird is a victim of lead-poisoning, probably ingested when it consumed a poisoned carcass left out by a farmer as bait for the coyotes that prey on livestock. The dead condor was found only because it had a radio-transmitter attached

the remaining condors into captivity, breed them and eventually reintroduce their progeny to the hills and deserts that constitute the southern Californian landscape. Others, the preservationists, sought only to increase protection for the last wild birds by extending their habitat and banning hunting.

Surely, claimed the antagonists, there was no point in playing God with only one piece of the jigsaw. Nature is about whole ecosystems interacting in multitudinous ways that, even with the most sophisticated technology, we're not even close to understanding. There's even a theory, formulated by English physicist James Lovelock, that the entire Earth is a self regulating organism – the so-called Gaia hypothesis. With that in mind, the old condor really is an ecological drop in the proverbial Pacific. Anyway, isolating one species could divert funds from wild populations and places. Dollars would be better spent on field conservation, habitat acquisition and reserve support, rather than putting animals into zoos.

The thorny issue of zoological gardens and captive breeding generates passionate feelings both pro and con. Many people fear that animals in zoos will lose their natural behaviour over several generations of captive breeding. In a mental and physical sense the condors might lose the adaptive qualities of their wild counterparts, soaring over the sierras with beady eyes in incessant pursuit of carrion. There are also the genetic problems manifest in propagating small populations. Inbreeding, hybridisation of subspecies and artificial selection for such traits as 'tameness' and 'easiness to manage', all deplete a population's genetic diversity so that future progeny are increasingly disparate from their free-living ancestors.

Both sides claimed the moral high ground for their solutions. Antagonists thought the birds should be allowed to die with dignity in the wild rather than serve time behind bars. The condor had become such a symbol of freedom and wilderness that its public image was almost cloaked in mysticism. In reality, it is a somewhat lethargic creature, so indifferent to people that individual birds have been known to share sandwiches with hikers crossing the Sespe mountains.

The raison d'être of Snyder and the zoo people was, and is, "better bred than dead". They knew that reintroduction would never be the whole answer, and that it is costly and difficult to undertake. They also knew that reintroduction worked best when pressures were at the species, not the habitat, level. For example, the Arabian oryx had been wiped out by hunters and not by its homelands disappearing.

For the condors, the pressures came from both levels. We have already mentioned the hunters, so what about the habitat? There is evidence that condor country was contracting well before people were around. Climatic changes, associated with the Ice Age's waning glaciers 7,000-10,000 years ago were ultimately responsible for shifting patterns of vegetation. Today, the pressure comes from California's human population that has vastly expanded since the Second World War.

Condors need large areas in which to live. They nest on inaccessible rocky ledges in rugged mountains. An individual may range several hundred kilometres in search of dead animals to eat. Much of their former habitat is farmland without the buffalo, elk and others whose deceased provided rich pickings as recently as 200 years ago.

The Sespe Condor Sanctuary is an exceptionally rugged region, where condors have done much of their breeding over the years. The last pair of condors known in the wild was located here

With fast growing cities like Ventura, Bakersfield and Santa Barbara, the condor was hemmed in. Throughout the 1970s, grazing land that once extended south from the condor's nesting sites to the edge of Los Angeles was engulfed in a spreading sea of suburban sprawl. When Noel Snyder visited the Sespe Condor Sanctuary in 1980, only one pair of the big birds were in residence. "When Karl Koford undertook his pioneering condor studies between the wars and into the 1950s, there were perhaps a dozen pairs or more in the sanctuary," said Snyder. "He had observations of more than thirty birds at a time on several occasions. His maximum was something like forty-two birds.

"Now we have a single pair and this split up in the last few months. We're hoping it may reform."

The Sespe Condor Sanctuary was set up as a result of Koford's studies. It used to be the primary nesting area for the species ... but just setting aside a sanctuary was not enough to save the condor.

"There was, I think, a lot of hope that by locking this area up and keeping out people completely, it would provide enough protection for the species," says Snyder. "Unfortunately this has not proved the case. The condors nest here but, when they forage, they fly off to the rangelands and that's where the problems start."

Witnessing the Sanctuary's inadequacies, and knowing the big bird better than most, only strengthened Snyder's interventionist zeal. For three decades the question: "to breed or not to breed?" had raged across the meeting rooms and offices of auspicious bodies like the National Audubon Society, the Zoological Societies of San Diego and Los Angeles, the US Fish and Wildlife Service and the California Department of Fish and Game. Finally the interventionists won.

At half past twelve in the afternoon of 30 June 1980, five scientists from the United States government gradually edged their way down a precipitous rock face. Their task: to undertake what they thought would be a routine examination of development and parasites. Their target: one of the only two nests that was known to contain a Californian condor chick. The scientists were from the Condor Recovery Team, and were led by Noel Snyder. Their intervention caused undue stress to the chick, and two hours later it was dead of heart failure.

This was exceedingly bad luck but, in the storm of protest that ensued, you might be forgiven for thinking that Snyder's team had committed a war crime. At one stage their newly acquired state and federal trapping permits were revoked, and it looked as though last year's condor would become this year's dodo.

Three years later, Snyder came back. In 1983 and 1984, several chicks were collected and eggs were removed from four wild condor pairs to encourage the laying of further clutches. In 1985 a fifth pair was discovered in the population and similarly manipulated to increase egg production.

All too aware of past mistakes and fearful of becoming the conservationists who dealt the *coup de grâce*, Snyder's team established hides near condor nests and watched the parents to glean a few lessons in condor mother care.

It seems that the rearing raptors were often just as dozy as everybody else when it came to looking after their chicks. One pair had produced a single bluish-white egg but

This pair of Californian condors are sunning themselves near their nest

were forever squabbling over whose turn it was to incubate it. They just couldn't agree, and any changeover from one parent to another only followed long, drawn out hassle.

One day the inevitable happened. Sitting in incredulous disbelief, Helen Snyder, an observer from the National Audubon Society, witnessed the predictable altercations when one parent returned to the nest. Californian condors incubate eggs by placing them on top of their feet. Startling the bird can cause it to kick the egg out of the nest. This time, the bumbling big bird kicked the precious egg into the air. Splat! Seconds later the yolk and white dribbled to oblivion over a nearby rocky ledge.

The condors couldn't have cared less. It might just as well not have happened as far as they were concerned. The only winners were the cackling ravens who beelined to a raw omelette dinner more expensive than that served at Maxims.

A month later, this Taylor and Burton of birds had made up and produced a second egg. This is known as double clutching. Normally birds lay one clutch of eggs and incubate it. If the eggs are lost or destroyed, they often produce a second, or even a third, clutch. Knowledge of this biological phenomenon had enabled Snyder to increase condor production by removing the first, and sometimes second, clutches from their nests.

Something else was also keen to remove eggs from condor nests by this stage. The ravens had become nouveau gastronomes. The embryo of the dodgy parents didn't stand a chance. No one appears to know the full story – it may have been another kick or even a reckless raven brave enough to dive-bomb the big birds' nest. The upshot was that another expensive egg disappeared down a corvid's crop.

Perhaps the raven's actions did do some good. That, and the incompetence of the breeding condor pairs, combined to fuel the interventionists' arguments and strengthen their case. Then, in late 1984 and early 1985, four of the remaining five wild condor pairs died out and four of the five human collaborating organisations dived in. All agreed that the remaining wild birds should be placed in captivity until better protection could be afforded in the field.

The only dissenter was the National Audubon Society, who managed to obtain a temporary restraining order prohibiting capture of the birds. Shortly after this, AC-3, the last wild breeding female, died at the San Diego Wild Animal Park where she had been taken for treatment for lead poisoning. The Federal Court ruled against the National Audubon Society. The last wild condor was captured on 19 April 1987.

Prior to this, techniques had been established to locate, capture and transport condor eggs – a tricky task. First Snyder's Condor Recovery Team had to locate the breeding pair and remove the first egg to stimulate double clutching. Finding nests was hard enough and often involved weeks of scrambling around the mountains while the capricious condors chose between a number of sites scattered over hundreds of square kilometres.

Here Bill Toone and Noel Snyder are carrying the first condor egg to be taken for artificial incubation.

Once a nest was discovered, it was kept under constant observation and then, at the right moment, the egg had to be snatched before marauding ravens, black bears or even the inept parents could finish it off. Sometimes golden eagles have been known to take nestlings.

A helicopter landing site was hurriedly hacked out of the dense, thorny bush – the mesquite – characteristic of condor country. Then the final approach to the nest was made with the greatest caution. Noel Snyder had learned the hard way to adopt a softly softly approach around condor nests. The biologists had no choice but to wait until the nest was unattended. The right moment only presented itself once every five or six days when both birds were off the egg.

The precious egg was carried in a specially designed case equipped with foam rubber padding, hot water bottles and thermometers; a cargo as precious as the crown jewels. It had to arrive not only intact but also at the right temperature. Transported by helicopter, the priceless cargo was off to a new home.

Thirty miles from the southern Californian naval town of San Diego roam herds of exotic antelopes, rhinoceroses, elephants and groups of western lowland gorillas. The local vegetation is high chaparral, a brush covered landscape familiar to anyone who watches cowboy movies. But forget about Clint Eastwood and the terrain could be Africa.

This is the San Diego Wild Animal Park, a country cousin to the world famous San Diego Zoo as Whipsnade is to London Zoo. The 1,800 acre park was opened in 1972 and visitors circumnavigate its vast expanses by means of an all electric, pollution-free monorail.

The San Diego Wild Animal Park - white rhino, waterbuck and giraffe in the East Africa exhibition

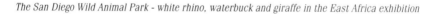

The `Condorminium' condor enclosure at San Diego Wild Animal Park. This building covers a quarter of a hectare, and contains the best facilities and information available for the successful breeding of wild birds

High up on a hill overlooking San Diego's very own Serengeti is a high security hotel, cosseted from the outside world by menacing coils of barbed wire and massive padlocks. The intention is to keep unwelcome visitors out as well as the inhabitants in. It's rather similar to those heavily fortressed havens that protect the film stars of Beverly Hills a hundred or more kilometres up the coast.

The huge complex covers about a quarter of a hectare. Christened the 'Condorminium' – but dubbed the 'Condortration Camp' by zoo keepers – it contains all the experience that San Diego's biologists have built up on the breeding of New World vultures together with the best of facilities from the Animal Park's Avian Propagation Centre which has a worldwide reputation for the successful breeding of wild birds.

It is here that the condor eggs are handled by embryologists who learned their skills with similar but less rare birds like Andean condors, black, king and turkey vultures. Under conditions of strict security, because no risks can be taken on programmes as costly and highly sensitive as this, the scientists go about their work. One of them is Bill Toone, San Diego Wild Animal Park's Curator of Birds. When *Nature Watch* visited him, he took Julian Pettifer through the early days of each condor egg.

"When an egg's delivered, we take it directly up to the hill, and it goes immediately into an incubator," said Toone. "At that time the egg will be candled – that is, we shoot a focused beam of light through the egg. This allows us not only to see if there's any

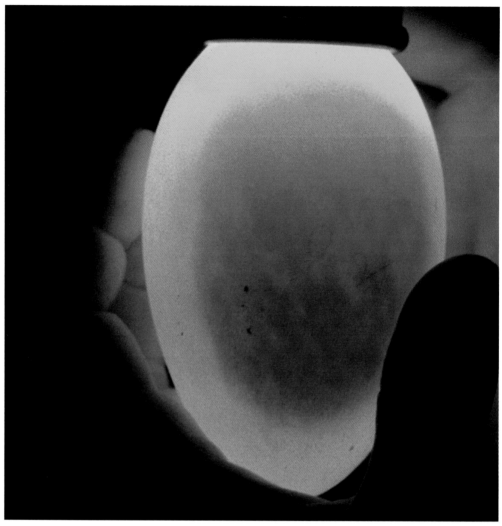

The condor eggs are candled to check that development is proceeding and to show up any cracks or breaks in the egg

development taking place, to aid us in determining whether it's fertile or not, but also will show any cracks or breaks in the egg that might not be visible without the light going through them."

Julian Pettifer asked whether, when the time comes, Bill helps the chick at all or whether they hatch of their own accord.

"Well, that also has varied from egg to egg, particularly in our first year. It was necessary to help three of the four chicks in the first year. In the second year quite a number of the chicks were helped but it was more a question of whether or not the risk of letting them do it on their own was too great."

To gain experience of the actual hatching, Bill's technicians practised with hundreds of live chicken eggs. This was in addition to scores of routine hatchings of other bird species in the zoo. The effort has paid off. More than 80% of the eggs taken for incubation have produced surviving condors – a success rate much higher than the 40-50 per cent achieved in the wild. But this is only the beginning of the story.

The chicks are destined, if at all possible, to return to the wild; to be released and to re-establish a wild population of condors. If that is to happen, then a great deal of care must be taken with their upbringing so that they can one day adapt to conditions outside the zoo. Above all, they must not be improperly imprinted – they must not grow up regarding their human captors as their parents, because that might inhibit their breeding behaviour in the wild. San Diego has solved the problem in a particularly inventive way, as Bill Toone explains:

"Here at the Park we've experimented with an arm glove puppet that looks like an adult parent condor. The puppet was made by keepers at the Wild Animal Park and has served us well over the last couple of years.

"We don't use the puppet during the actual break out of the egg but it's around immediately afterwards. Again the break out process with the value of these birds is so critical that it's felt that anything that would mess up our manual dexterity we don't get involved in, but as soon as that part is over with the puppet comes right on in and takes over the role as mum."

The ever-hungry condor chicks soon become imprinted on the glove puppet. They never see the faces of their surrogate parents. "What we do," says Bill Toone, "is we put up an opaque barrier between the chick and the keepers and, after the chick has broken out, everything that occurs with that chick is done with the puppet, including some social interactions. The chick is fed with the puppet, the towels that are round it are taken out and cleaned by the puppet and, in fact, many times when there's no work to do, which is rare, the puppet goes in and simply messes around, preens the chick and there's a great deal of social interaction that goes on to help cement the bond between the chick and the puppet."

Julian Pettifer enquired as to the exact nature of the young birds' diet. Just what would a newly hatched condor accept as suitable fare? Bill Toone was ready with a surprising answer:

"Well, that involves another

Naturewatcher Bill Toone, San Diego Wild Animal Park's Curator of Birds with a condor glove puppet. The puppet is used so that chicks do not become imprinted on humans as parents

interesting technique. That was a question that was put to me before the programme started. My boss asked me to come up with a diet for young condors and I read the literature where there's all sorts of very complex diets of things you can feed vultures, but the fact of the matter is that in the wild the mum simply regurgitates food for the birds. Vultures, because of their eating habits where they'll eat a great deal of food at one time, in fact often so much that it impairs their flying ability, have evolved a fascinating response when threatened by a predator. They just up-chuck their grub to lighten the load, and go. We found here at the Park that all it takes is to show 'em a net, everybody throws up, we go in and pick up the vomit and feed it to the babies which works out great!"

At nearby Los Angeles Zoo, there's another flourishing community of captive bred condors. Again security is tight and the birds are under constant observation. Either the eye of the television camera or that of the scientific observer is recording their activities day and night. One of the patient condor watchers is Dr Cathleen Cox who, in the course of her work, has become a mistress of subterfuge, stealth and disguise.

When *Nature Watch* visited the Los Angeles Zoo, Julian Pettifer had to don a Friesian cow suit in order to approach the big birds. They must never be allowed to become familiar with, and unafraid of, the threatening outline of humans. The cow suit was developed as a result of extensive trials that involved camouflaging the keepers in a variety of tube-like costumes. Other prototypes provided unsuitable to work in as they restricted the keepers' movement. The cow suit was flexible enough to allow the keepers to move their hands ... and it certainly fooled the chicks.

This is Molloko, the first Californian condor chick to be bred from captive parents, with its puppet feeder

Noel Snyder with Julian Pettifer and Cathleen Cox from Los Angeles Zoo. Condor chicks must never be allowed to become familiar with and unafraid of humans - hence the Friesian cow disguises!!

The released condors are a bit different from the wild birds because each one of them is radio tagged and followed every single day. Someone will be there to save them if trouble looms.

The captive condor population now rests at 52 birds. Eleven of the twelve potential breeding pairs produced twenty-two eggs during the 1991 breeding season. Seventeen were fertile and thirteen hatched. In light of the population increase, the Condor Recovery Team recommended to the US Fish and Wildlife Service that two condors be released to the wild in December 1991. Both birds will be taking full advantage of H.R. 2556. H.R. 2556 is the anonymous number that holds the key to the condor's future. Translated as the Los Padres Condor Range and River Protection Act, it designates 398,000 acres in California's Los Padres National Forest as protected wilderness, including former condor habitat. It also designates 50 kilometres of streams (on Sespe Creek, Sisquoc River and Big Sur River) as wild and scenic rivers which also protects these areas from development. The bill was approved on 10 October 1991.

The two condors, one hatched at each of San Diego and Los Angeles zoos, were released with two young female Andean condors to increase the size of the group and to facilitate appropriate movements and behaviour.

Five years ago, Noel Snyder said, "We're hopeful. We think we're probably in time. It remains to be seen if this intervention can save the Californian condor from extinction." His actions have been vindicated. The condor watch is no longer a death watch. The big birds are back.

Naturewatcher Mike Donoghue works for New Zealand's Department of Conservation, managing the protection of marine mammals

SEALS, SQUID AND SUSTAINABLE SEAS

Seen from space, our planet appears predominantly blue. The oceans are the dominant feature, covering almost three quarters of its surface. Yet, as land lubbers we have named the planet 'Earth'. Planet 'Sea' would be a more fitting title.

Naturewatcher Mike Donoghue spends most of his working life fighting for the survival of marine ecosystems. Mike works in New Zealand where he manages the protection of marine mammals for the Department of Conservation. Attaining a balance between the fishing industry and conservation is a continuing theme in his mission to save the southern oceans.

The seas are special and essential for our survival. They play a key role in the hydrological cycle, the chemistry of the atmosphere and the formation of climate and weather. Within the waves lies a vital food source, a network of shipping lanes, a playground, and an important supply of energy, minerals and medicine.

Human activities, both inland and in coastal regions, are already causing rapid deterioration of marine ecosystems and resources in many parts of the world. Poorly planned industrial, urban and agricultural development modify and pollute the seas. River dams and deforestation alter salinity and sedimentation rates in coastal zones. In fact, over three quarters of marine pollution originates from the land via rivers, direct discharge and the atmosphere. The rest comes from dumping, shipping, offshore mining and oil production.

Overfishing and the hunting of marine mammals also exact a heavy toll. During the 1980s, the world marine fish catch increased steadily to a peak of eighty-four million tonnes in 1988. Many fish stocks are fully fished, and overfishing helped by new technology and fluctuating fish populations has led to the decline and instability of many fisheries worldwide.

The enormity of the oceans is such that it is easy to think of them as limitless providers, immune to our plundering and poisoning. But this is not so. Most of the life in the sea is concentrated along relatively narrow strips formed by the continental shelves, coastal margins and estuaries. In these areas are found a wealth of productive and diverse habitats like mangroves, saltmarshes, mudflats, seagrass and coral reefs. Such places protect fragile coastlines and function as nurseries, restaurants, and boarding houses for numerous fish, molluscs and crustaceans that account for over two

The Coromandel Peninsula is in New Zealand's North Island, and is one of Mike Donoghue's favourite places with its varied and closely balanced ecosystems. The vegetation here has suffered greatly over the last 150 years from human disturbance

thirds of world fisheries production. Coastal zones have the highest biological productivity levels on Earth and yield over eighty per cent of the world's fishing catch. Further, they are home to most of the world's population who depend on their resources and determine their ecological 'health'. Two thirds of the world's cities, with populations exceeding two and a half million people are located near tidal estuaries. Sixty per cent of humanity lives within sixty kilometres of coastal waters.

Yet most people have no idea about how much they depend on oceans or what their impact is upon them. Until recently, the management and science of the seas were the responsibilities of a few specialists. Some specialists, like Mike Donoghue, are now working to make sure they concern us all.

One of Mike's favourite spots is the Coromandel Peninsula, in New Zealand's North Island, about sixty kilometres from Auckland as the albatross glides. "It's just a magic place," he says. "It's the proximity of the bush and the trees to the sea. You have all those different ecosystems so closely balancing each other."

Walking through Coromandel gives Mike the space to breathe and time to think about the challenges of his demanding job. The area has taught him many lessons about the changing nature of New Zealand's environment. He contemplates what it was like before the Polynesians and first Europeans arrived. "Apart from the huge flightless moas, there was a profusion – a real abundance – of marine mammals and fish here. The general opinion is that,before human exploitation began, we probably had about sixty thousand southern right whales around these shores. Today, if we're lucky and after sixty years of protection there's perhaps three thousand left.

"Most of what we know comes from the anecdotal logs of whaling ship skippers. There's a famous story of a skipper who sailed out from Sydney and counted fifteen thousand whales in his first three days on the Tasman Sea. That's probably more than the total number of those species in the entire world now."

On the mainland there has also been terrible destruction since the early European settlers arrived in Coromandel. Some of it is linked to the fate of the marine mammals. A lot of it centres around a tree called the kauri.

Six hundred years ago, the entire Coromandel Peninsula was full of huge kauri trees. A few still remain – giant, ancient podocarps, which are trees unique to New Zealand.

The destruction began in a big way during the 1850s and 60s. Kauri wood was used for building houses in Auckland and Thames and the other towns that were springing up all over New Zealand. Early whaling vessels docked in the local bays and replenished their masts and spas with kauri. Eventually entire whaling ships were built from the indigenous tree, only to return to sea and hunt many of the whale species to the very brink of extinction.

After the initial felling of kauri trees, there was a big gold rush in the Coromandel area during the 1860s. Much of the land was cleared and even fewer of the giant kauri remained. Many of the survivors were chopped down at the beginning of the twentieth century to rebuild San Francisco following the big earthquake and fire in 1906. After that, people came along and dug up the roots to extract gum which was used in Kiwi boot polish.

Six hundred years ago the whole of the Coromandel Peninsula was full of these huge kauri trees. Human destruction has led to only a handful of the original trees remaining

Very few kauri trees survived the onslaught, but a handful of the originals remain today, and the area has largely recovered from former plundering. "I suppose some enlightened person in those days decided they'd better leave perhaps one per cent of what was once here," says Mike Donoghue. "We're very lucky to have these big kauris here now."

The story of Coromandel is not something that Mike Donoghue wants to see repeated in the southern oceans. It is not enough to effectively ravage an area and leave a mere one per cent in the hope it lasts for posterity. Mike's goal is something different. It's called sustainable development.

Sustainable development is at the forefront of modern conservation philosophy, policy and practice. It recognises that development and conservation are not sworn enemies. Rather, they should be integrated and work with, not against, each other.

Much current development fails because it meets human needs incompletely and often destroys or degrades its resource base (think of those kauri trees). Sustainable development is people-centred. It aims to provide real improvements in the quality of human life. After all, people work and manipulate the seas. Such places provide their livelihood. If you do not have the will and support of these people, you can forget about saving the seas. Alternatively, if you show people how to use the sea as a truly renewable resource, and they discover that, by doing this, their business has a long term future – a sort of environmental security of tenure – *and* a viable economic base, then maybe the oceans will survive in a healthy state for many more millennia.

Sustainable development must be conservation-based. It is concerned about maintaining the variety and productivity of nature. True sustainable development and sustainable living is about handing at least as much of the environment as we inherited from our immediate ancestors to the next and future generations. The good news is that, if people adopt a strategy of sustainable living, individually, collectively, locally and globally, we need not lose the battle for the planet.

This is the greatest challenge facing humanity today. It is continually debated in conservation's corridors of power. It features in keynote speeches of international environmental organisations and governments. It is the main thrust of 'Caring for the Earth', a major world conservation strategy launched by the World Conservation Union (IUCN), Worldwide Fund for Nature (WWF) and United Nations Environment Programme (UNEP) in 1991.

It all seems a long way from Mike Donoghue but it isn't at all. Even when Mike takes his boat down the coast and goes fishing, he's thinking sustainably.

Mike used to be a fisherman. It was an unusual job for a city born lad and armchair academic. "When I came to live in this place, I really liked it so much that I wanted to stay. There weren't any jobs for academics so it was a question of having to make a living and fishing was the only thing that presented itself that seemed attractive."

Mike's method of fishing is highly selective. He uses lines and hooks that are specifically targeted to capture snapper of a particular size. On the hooks are placed chunks of octopus – favoured by the snappers and handy for the fishermen because, although it takes ages to chop up, octopus stays on the hooks a long time. The best time to drop the hooks and lines is during a change of light so dawn and dusk are

Large scale fishing and trawling pose a huge threat to marine mammals as they easily get caught up in the vast nets

usually the preferred fishing periods. Often, Mike has to weigh the line down with stones to make the hooks sink faster. "We have to get them away quickly from opportunist shearwaters and other sea birds who try and take the octopus off the hook," he says. "Mind you, we always try to avoid setting when there are birds around. It's not a pleasant experience to capture them."

When Mike fished full time, he would set and retrieve fifteen hundred to two thousand hooks during a working day. Now, he fishes largely for fun and only sets five or six hundred hooks during each day's trip. "I really love being here," he says whilst pulling in the lines, "but it's real hard work. The good times just about make up for the bad, but I wouldn't really relish the idea of doing it two hundred days a year again."

After landing a fish, Mike 'spikes' it with a screwdriver. "It's not a pretty sight but it is humane. It kills the fish by destroying the brain," he says. "There's also the economic consideration. Spiking the fish produces a much better fillet that keeps longer. I'm looking for particularly colourful fish about ten or twelve years old. I put them in a slurry of ice and seawater kept at between three and three and a half degrees Celsius. That's the best temperature for preserving the tissues. Then the fish will be air freighted to Japan without being frozen and will be on sale for the Japanese sushi market within forty-eight hours of leaving the sea."

The small time fishermen don't get rich but they do make a reasonable living. Mike thinks their approach is sustainable because it is so selective, there is much less wasteful incidental killing than when huge trawl nets are used, the fishing equipment is recoverable – it doesn't drift aimlessly in the ocean killing anything unfortunate enough to get in its way, and the fishers themselves have a decent quality of life in superb surroundings.

Experience as a fisherman has certainly helped Mike to get to grips with his current career of saving the seas and the marine mammals. "I understand a lot of the technical details involved in fishery operations," he says, "and I know about the problems involved with big time fishing, particularly when you have interactions with non target species like dolphins, birds or other fish. The fishermen know me. They know that I've paid my dues."

One of the marine mammals whose survival is directly threatened by the fishing industry is Hooker's sealion. It is the world's rarest sealion species, extremely restricted in distribution, and has already escaped extinction once. As Mike Donoghue says:

"It's the marine mammal species that gives me most cause for concern at the moment. We don't know how many there once were but we do know that they were formerly distributed throughout the North and South Islands. That's until the nineteenth century commercial sealers came along and hunted them to the brink of extinction before they received protection. Even though the sealions have worse pelts than the fur seals, the sealers still killed them."

Today, Hooker's sealion is confined to the Auckland Islands, some two hundred kilometres south of New Zealand's South Island in the sub Antarctic. The trouble is that, over the last fifteen years, a big squid fishery has developed in the area. Unlike most squid fisheries, who use a technique called jigging to catch the squid, this one uses trawlers. Every year Japanese, Korean and Russian trawlers fish the seas at exactly the

This is a male Hooker's sealion, the world's rarest sealion species. It is extremely restricted in its distribution, and at high risk from the squid fisheries

same time as the sealions are breeding. Past records indicate that for every fifty to one hundred trawls, a sealion is incidentally caught in the squid nets. Because so many boats work the area around the Auckland Islands, it works out that about a hundred sealions have been killed each year over the last decade and a half. Three-quarters of these are females who usually have a suckling pup on shore and a developing foetus in the womb. So each kill really means an effective loss of three animals.

"One of the big problems is that these sealions are particularly good divers who can dive to depths of four hundred metres and will do so repeatedly when feeding for up to sixty hours at a time," says Mike Donoghue. "The entire time that the trawl net is in the water, even at those great depths, the animals are vulnerable. Because the species is so restricted in its distribution and because they all return to the same beaches to breed, all the females are at risk of entanglement and drowning during the suckling period. You see, when mum's producing milk, she needs the energy rich squid diet to keep the milk flow going. Both the trawlers and the sealions are targeting the same squid in the same area."

It is incredibly difficult to monitor the situation. "Unless you have independent government observers on the boats, the skippers tend not to report sealion deaths," explains Mike. "Either the skippers haven't been told to report which is a particular problem in New Zealand where we have a lot of foreign vessels operating, or they keep quiet because if word gets out about how many sealions are dying, then the fishery will be in jeopardy. The result is we now believe that the sealion population hasn't increased in the last fifteen years. In fact, there are fears that it may be declining – perhaps at a rate that will cause the species to become extinct within fifty to sixty years."

Mike's bottom line is to conserve the sealion, but he wants to resolve the conflict in a sustainable way; one which will allow for the continuance of an economic industry. He thinks that there are two ways to achieve this.

"One possibility is to investigate harvesting the squid by some other fishing method. Most of the world's squid fisheries use something called jigging. That's where you put coloured lures with a crown of hooks in the water and jig them up and down. The squid confuse the movement and colour with that of their prey, and throw themselves onto the hooks. As far as we can judge, jigging doesn't pose a hazard to sealions. The drawback is that the seas around Auckland Island are very rough. It would be more difficult to catch squid by jigging than by trawling, and some of the larger trawlers would find it hard to stay in operation during the summer months.

"The other important thing is to know scientifically what's going on. We've received some very helpful advice from the United States who have given us clear guidelines on how to work out what might be an acceptable incidental catch of sealions – one that would still allow the population to recover and sustain itself at a viable level. It seems to be about one third of the incidental catch of the last fifteen years."

Mike thinks that the sealions and the squid fishery can co-exist in harmony. He knows that the final decision rests with the New Zealand government but has faith in the Department of Conservation and public opinion to effect change. "It's great that, in a country with unemployment problems and a need to generate overseas revenue, the

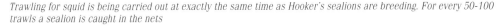

Trawling for squid is being carried out at exactly the same time as Hooker's sealions are breeding. For every 50-100 trawls a sealion is caught in the nets

Hooker's sealions are not the only victims of drift net fishing for squid. This is a baby swordfish which got entangled

people have overwhelmingly said that the protection of Hooker's Sealion takes precedence over economic considerations." The 1993 squid fishing season around the Auckland Islands provided encouraging results, with only 12 sealions taken during the whole season. Mike is hopeful that the combination of public concern for the future of the sealion and an increasingly responsible attitude of the fishing industry bodes well for the future of the New Zealand sealion.

Seals played an important part in the early European settlement of New Zealand. The New Zealand fur seal – a species closer to sealions than true seals – was highly prized for its thick fur. Even Captain Cook told tales of vast numbers of fur seals. The sealing vessels would come in, drop off a sealing gang for a year or two, and they would go around systematically clubbing the seals on the colonies before skinning them and drying the skins. A lot of the pelts went to Europe where they were fashioned into the fur bands around hats.

In the first few years of the nineteenth century, some quarter of a million fur seals were taken from New Zealand and surrounding sub Antarctic islands. One vessel, the 'Brothers', went into Sydney in 1806 with eighty thousand fur seal skins and came back two years later with another sixty thousand. That equates to about two and a half times the current total population of the species. In the end, only ten thousand New Zealand fur seals remained – ninety-five per cent of the world total had been killed.

The species received full legal protection in 1891 and current estimates suggest that thirty-five to forty thousand individuals swim in the southern oceans. Like their sealion relative, they too have to keep dodging the trawl nets.

New Zealand fur seals are in danger from fishermen trawling for hoki. In 1989 and 1990 about 1500 fur seals were taken in trawls

"The most obvious effect of humans on the New Zealand fur seal comes from the deep-water trawl fishery for hoki," says Mike Donoghue. "Hoki is a deep water fish that lives all round New Zealand. Off the west coast of South Island they come in huge spawning aggregations of a million tonnes or more, and in the last ten years the hoki fishery in the area has become New Zealand's largest volume fishery. Some of the trawlers tow nets that can engulf the Bank of New Zealand building in Wellington. That's our country's tallest building. In 1989 and 1990 about fifteen hundred fur seals were taken in the trawls."

Once again, fishermen and seals are competing for the same resource at the same time. As the fish are hauled up from the depths, seals, attracted by the noise and spillage of offal, become entangled in the nets and drown. The hoki quota was increased to a quarter of a million tonnes in 1989. Not sustainable, say the conservationists.

"This is a case where the killing is accidental," says Mike Donoghue. "It's not a question of the fishermen targeting the seals. The seals are targeting the fishing boats. In fact the industry is very anxious to avoid the problem. They've changed their fishing practices and they're experimenting with a sonic seal scarer developed by a Swedish company. I'm pleased to say that in the season that's just finished, the catch was certainly way down and we're all feeling a little bit more comfortable about it. But two hundred seals a year are still being killed and we have to tell the fishermen to watch the rubbish they chuck over the sides of their boats. The plastic bands found around bait boxes can be lethal necklaces for seals who swim into them. The plastic cuts in deeper and deeper until the seal can't feed properly any more or is strangled."

During his career, Mike Donoghue has waged an all out war on unselective drift netting. "Drift net vessels are not especially large," he says, "but they deploy around fifty kilometres of very thin nylon net that just drifts on the ocean surface. When you have five hundred boats a night deploying enough net to stretch around the entire world and across the Pacific again, you have very serious problems. Everything that swims into a drift net becomes enmeshed.

"Luckily all the South Pacific nations had a very strong stand against the introduction of drift nets into their waters. One reason was that the countries that decided to start using them in our region never consulted anyone, and second, the South Pacific nations realised their marine resources were in mortal danger."

When the New Zealand public learned about the wasteful carnage, they were incensed. The figures made depressing reading. As Mike Donoghue explains, "Just in the Tasman Sea, we think we had about twenty thousand dolphins killed in two seasons by entanglement in drift nets. Even that pales into insignificance against the global picture of up to half a million dolphins and small whales taken each year."

In 1989 the New Zealand government banned the use or possession of drift nets in its waters. Although the ban is largely symbolic – most drift netting is undertaken in international waters – it reflected the growing abhorrence for indiscriminate fishing methods used by the Japanese, Taiwanese and Koreans. The example set by the South Pacific nations, however, sparked a global outcry, involving the United Nations. Under

Mammals such as these dusky dolphins risk becoming enmeshed in a drift net

intense pressure, the Asian driftnetters agreed to end all drift net fishing in international waters by the end of 1992. It was Mike Donoghue's finest hour and greatest conservation victory.

But in his quest to save the seas, Mike Donoghue is not a man to stand still. In the mid 1980s, another type of net and another marine mammal caught his attention.

Hector's dolphin is New Zealand's only endemic dolphin – found nowhere else in the world. When a couple of postgraduate students monitored the species, they discovered that the total population was only three to four thousand, and that the largest breeding colony at Banks' Peninsula near Christchurch was under severe stress from the effects of entanglement in gill nets.

Gill nets are anchored to the ocean floor. They consist of a plastic so thin that the dolphins often don't see them until it is too late. As slow reproducing mammals, dolphin populations cannot afford additional human induced mortality. Hector's dolphin numbers around Banks Peninsula were cut by one third over a single five year period. Some of the reports given to researchers by the fishermen masked the true extent of the damage.

New Zealand's Department of Conservation were quick to respond. They established the country's first marine mammal sanctuary around Banks Peninsula. Within the sanctuary there is no commercial gill netting allowed and amateur gill nets are only permitted during the winter months when the dolphins are not close inshore. "The amateur fishers protested long and loud about unfair discrimination," says Mike Donoghue, "but we're only talking at most about a few hundred people. The plus side is that Hector's dolphin has caught the public's imagination. They've become the marine

Hector's dolphin is New Zealand's only endemic dolphin. Its population is under stress from gill netting, so the Department of Conservation established the country's first marine mammal sanctuary around Banks Peninsula. Within this sanctuary no commercial gill netting is allowed

equivalent of kakapos. They've appeared on health stamps, and a well known British multinational company has adopted them and sponsored a research programme."

Since the sanctuary was established, Banks Peninsula has become much more popular as a tourist destination, just like Kaikoura, a traditional fishing community and whaling town on the north-east coast of South Island. "Earlier this century, sperm whales were killed here," says Mike Donoghue. "During the 1980s, Kaikoura's economy declined and the place became a pit-stop for truckies on the way from Picton to Christchurch. But Kaikoura has transformed its economy within the last three years. It's a major tourist destination built on the backs of whales, seals and dolphins."

Fifteen species of whales and dolphins occur in the waters off Kaikoura, and some half a million people now visit the town each year. They go to watch the seal colonies, migrating sperm whales and dusky dolphins. They bring in an estimated annual five million dollars of tourist income and have totally revitalised the town.

"It's ironic in a way," says Mike Donoghue. "These seals used to be the bane of these fishermen's lives. They were accused of being the rabbits of the sea. As the marine resources were increasingly thrashed, the fishermen had to work harder for fewer returns. Now the marine mammals generate more revenue for Kaikoura than fishing ever did."

Mike's work will never be finished. Whale-watching is booming but Mike must make sure that the ecotourists don't get too close and stress the leviathans. Outside New Zealand's waters, other whales and dolphins are in dire need of protection from the ever present threat of some nations to resume commercial whaling. This year Mike will be fighting for them at the conference table of the International Whaling Commission.

For now, he surveys the coast at Kaikoura and allows himself a rare moment of relaxation. "It's renewable and sustainable," he muses. "With a bit of care and attention, it will go on indefinitely. It's fantastic."

The beautiful natural tropical rainforest wilderness

CHAPTER NINE

TALKING TO TARZAN

Most of us will never sail up the Amazon, break bread in a Bornean Dyak longhouse or encounter the zoology of Zaire at first hand. We know about such places because of the wealth of wildlife books and natural history film footage currently available. TV programmes like *Nature Watch* have delivered the plight of the world's tropical forests to our front rooms.

Not so long ago, say three decades, it was all rather different. Most wildlife documentaries were shot in studios and featured 'animal men' holding stressed snakes and malevolent mongooses under the hot lights. Such distant memories are now relegated to the 'out-takes' shows where we cruelly relish the bit when the presenter gets bitten.

The jungle was different. It was brought to our neighbourhoods via Tarzan movies. Tarzan swung through the trees on huge vines and communed with the animals. Tarzan of the Apes was at home with non-human primates, but spoke monosyllabically to his own species. The bronzed Adonis, an American ex-Olympic athlete in real life until later films portrayed him as an exiled English aristocrat, looked great as he crashed through celluloid African rainforests stuffed to the gills with South American macaws and Asian elephants. Whatever happened to Tarzan?

Naturewatcher Russell Mittermeier - modern day Tarzan!

In a sense, Tarzan is alive and well in the guise of Naturewatcher Dr Russell Mittermeier, a dynamic, blue-eyed bronzed American; the action man of conservation. Russ is a primatologist; someone who studies monkeys, apes and lemurs. He is also a herpetologist, an expert on reptiles and amphibians. As a dedicated conservationist, the former director of the American World Wildlife Fund's primate programme and the present head of an organisation called Conservation International, Russ globetrots on a continual basis to visit conservation projects worldwide.

The latterday Tarzan still communes with monkeys and apes. Indeed, one magazine wrote an article about him entitled 'Russell of the Apes'. But he is equally at home staring at a computer screen or speaking at major conferences. His vines are not made of fibrous strangling figs, but modern grapevines that utilise the latest technology to stay ahead of developments in the field. This Greystoke does not grunt at his fellow men. Russ Mittermeier is fluent in six languages and a consummate politician, well versed in the skills of diplomacy, negotiation and communication that are essential at the interface of conservation, development, politics and big business. And he does not wear a loincloth either.

Mittermeier is a hard man to pin down. One day he could be in Boston, the next in Brazil. The *Nature Watch* team tracked him to Costa Rica where he and Julian Pettifer joined forces to take a stroll through the Manuel Antonio National Park, indulge in some monkey watching, and hear Russ expound upon the latest thinking at the sharp end of global conservation.

Costa Rica is a Central American country about two-fifths the size of England. Formerly over three-quarters of its land surface was covered with tropical forests, but much has been destroyed during the last three to four decades. Nevertheless, the country still harbours a bewildering array of animal and plant species including eight hundred and fifty types of bird from iridescent hummingbirds to huge rapacious harpy eagles. That is one hundred and fifty species more than in the entire North American continent.

Despite its size, Costa Rica has an enviable reputation for its farsighted conservation policies. Twenty-seven per cent of the land area is protected. There are forty-six wildlife parks and a number of Indian reserves. "It's an exceptional country in other ways," says Russ Mittermeier. "It was one of the first to come up with the idea of government financed education in the last century, and it abolished its army in 1948. Costa Rica really is a paradise stuck in the middle of an area that has been dominated by military leaders and unrest in the recent past. I'd like to see much of the world follow its example."

Within this crowning glory of central America, tucked in the south-western corner, is the pocket handkerchief sized Manuel Antonio National Park, a mass of dense vegetation, tumbling vines and tropical forest that extends right down to the ocean.

Manuel Antonio is surrounded by coconut palm plantations. "The area was altered by humans several times in the past before it received protection," says Russ Mittermeier. "There's a lot of introduced plant species that are not native to the area, but it's a perfectly adequate habitat for monkeys and other animals."

Quite a few 'other animals' were spotted as Russ and Julian Pettifer trod cautiously through the forest. "We've got to watch where we're stepping," said Russ as he explained about the abundance of one of South America's most venomous snakes, the fer-de-lance, in the area.

Suddenly Julian noticed a slender snouted green snake about one and a half metres in length. Russ, an accomplished herpetologist, identified it as a Central American vine snake. "Its local name means frog hunter," he said. "I think it probably eats more lizards than frogs. It's very adept at catching reptiles and amphibians in the trees. The

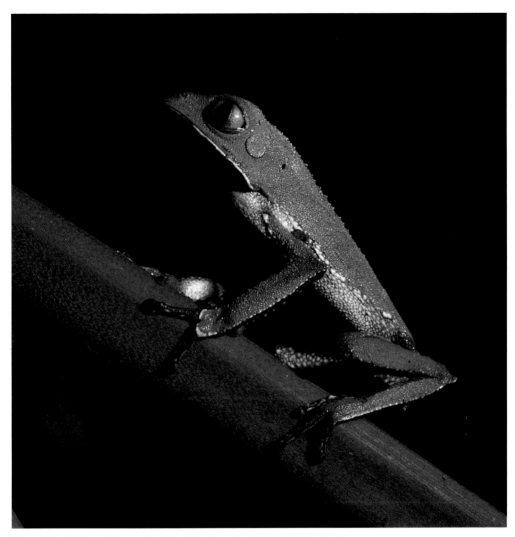

The rainforest is home to a great variety of spectacular wildlife - this is a tree frog

green colour serves as camouflage, and the species produces a mild poison that is good at slowing down its prey but not dangerous to people. It's really quite attractive, don't you think?"

Before Julian had time to think, Russ had rushed off, at home as only a new age Tarzan could be under the tropical sun. "Ah ha!" he exclaimed. "A basilisk lizard. Now this is really interesting. This animal can run on two legs across water for several metres at a stretch. Sometimes it's even called the Jesus Christ lizard.

"And that's an iguana – a very common lizard in central America that can grow up to two metres long including the tail. Iguanas are regularly eaten in this part of the world. It's an excellent meal, I've tried it myself. A very good source of protein and another species that does very well in a protected area like this."

This 2 toed sloth lives high in the rainforest trees, where it has very few natural predators and faces little competition from other animals

The next encounter slowed down the inexhaustible Mittermeier, and gave the *Nature Watch* crew a welcome break. "Look, there's a sloth," he beamed. "They're wonderful creatures and have some very strange habits. Even though they live high up in the trees, they descend to the forest floor once a week or so to defecate."

Arboreal or tree-dwelling animals usually just void their bowels wherever they happen to be at a particular time. No one knows why sloths should risk the momentous downward journey to their terra firma toilet, why they go to all the trouble of burying their droppings, and why they make themselves vulnerable to ground living predators. They are not exactly the Speedy Gonzalez of the animal kingdom. As Russ Mittermeier says, "The sloth ain't no competition for a cheetah."

In fact they are so lethargic that algae grows on them, providing food for a number of interesting parasites. Run your fingers through sloth fur and lots of little moths come flying out. Despite the laid back approach to life, sloths occupy a successful niche in South American forests. They eat leaves – mainly from Cecropia trees – and face little feeding competition from other animals. In addition they are surprisingly difficult to prey upon. "A sloth is very solid," says Russ Mittermeier. "The rib cage is like a brick. I've seen them falling out of trees and hit the ground from fifteen to twenty metres. They just move off as if nothing has happened. Although harpy eagles apparently take a lot of them, sloths are quite abundant throughout the Amazon and central America."

Also found in the area are monkeys. Manuel Antonio National Park harbours three species of them; the Central American howler monkey, capuchin monkey and squirrel monkey.

The latter species particularly concerns Russ Mittermeier. It is the most endangered Central American primate. "There are two geographical races or subspecies of this monkey," says Russ. "The one that occurs in Manuel Antonio is down to about five hundred and eighty individuals in the wild. Two hundred and eighty of those live in this particular reserve so you have roughly half of the remaining population in this tiny protected area."

The Manuel Antonio squirrel monkeys are reasonably secure at the moment. The remainder of the subspecies lives on private ranches and forests that could be cut down at some point in the future. But the park's primates thrive in the dense vegetation and tangled vines that constitute their habitat. Here they manoeuvre acrobatically through the branches, searching for small fruits and insects to eat. Sometimes the monkeys, particularly the capuchins, venture out to the surrounding plantations and feast on coconuts.

Russ Mittermeier's employer, Conservation International, is only six years old. In early 1990 it became the first international conservation organisation to develop a global strategy for rainforest conservation. This Rainforest Imperative concentrates on recognised conservation 'hotspot' areas and uses them as a focus for its projects in the tropics. "We're now active in a lot of hotspots like the Atlantic coastal forest region of Brazil and Madagascar," says Russ. "In all our conservation activities we place a special emphasis on working with local people. Although we're based in the United States, sixty per cent of our staff comes from Latin America and other tropical regions. Forty per cent of our directors are from the tropics. Our feeling is that if you don't develop solutions locally with local peoples and communities, then conservation won't work in the long term."

Costa Rica is high on Conservation International's list of priority hotspots. One of its activities has been to support researchers studying the Manuel Antonio squirrel monkeys and developing the park in environmentally friendly ways. Russ Mittermeier explains how this fits in with Conservation International's philosophy:

The Manuel Antonio National Park in Costa Rica harbours three money species, one of which is this capuchin

"All our programmes rest on five corner stones," he says. "First, scientific understanding. You can't achieve conservation unless you know about what you're trying to conserve. Second, protected area management. This is more or less traditional park and protected area management. Third comes conservation based development which looks at the interface between conservation and development. We try to find solutions that maximise both the variety of life and the economic benefits to local people and the countries in which these ecosystems occur. The next cornerstone is communication. We believe very strongly in using the power of the media, all forms of media, to get the word out as quickly as possible. We have to – there's so little time left in which to save the most endangered areas on the planet. Finally we try to influence development policy design and reform. So many conservation problems that we face in the tropics are based on unsound government policies like subsidies for cattle pasturing in the Amazon or inappropriate tax structures that actually encourage deforestation when they should be trying to prevent it.

"These different conservation techniques are woven together and the mix that we use depends very much on the needs and cultural sensitivities of the particular countries that we are working in."

The scientific understanding piece of the package takes quite a lot of effort, particularly if you are trying to observe small primates that never stay still in the convoluted undergrowth of the Manuel Antonio National Park. It's a case of first find your monkey.

Julian Pettifer and Russ Mittermeier set off with Grace Wong who has studied the squirrels for several years. "We'll probably hear them first," said Russ. "Listen for little squeaks and the sounds of animals bouncing around on branches." Then it was a matter of turning detective and searching out the characteristic signs that monkeys leave all over the place.

"This is a nancy fruit," said Russ. "It's a favourite food species of the squirrel here. You can sometimes find it in the local market. Hmmm – not bad. A little sour but quite tasty." Russ picked up another fruit. Monkeys are very messy and wasteful eaters. Dropped fruit with a mouthful or two taken out of it is a dead give away to their presence in the vicinity.

"Now that's what's called a hog plum. It's a very tasty fruit in the mango family," said Russ. "I find it quite delicious myself. It's one of the food species that people could harvest sustainably from the tropical forest ecosystem."

About an hour before dusk, the intrepid explorers finally located the objects of their search. Grace explained that the little yellow monkeys with agouti crowns and pasty clown faces belonged to her study

The squirrel monkey is the most endangered of the Central American primates, mainly as its habitat is threatened by destruction

group. It was difficult to see them all. Russ and Julian counted ten to twelve, but Grace said the entire troop contained about thirty animals. She could identify many of the individual monkeys from their natural markings. Males are particularly distinctive.

Julian noted that the group included a large number of juveniles. "They've been reproducing well of late," said Russ. "Of the fourteen known groups of this sub-species of Central American squirrel monkey, six occur within the Manuel Antonio National Park. Grace says that the species has increased in numbers here since the place was declared a National Park in 1972."

Squirrel monkeys prefer the lower and middle levels of tropical forests. Here they find the thick secondary regrowth that supports the highest densities of insects and other invertebrates that provide juicy, protein rich meals. Grace has recorded thirty types of fruit that the monkeys eat as well as three species of plant that are visited for their nectar.

Eating fast moving insects and patchily distributed fruit means that the squirrel monkeys have to be on the go all the time in order to satisfy their nutritional requirements. This contrasts sharply with the Park's larger howler monkeys. Howlers are the biggest monkeys in the area. Their enlarged bony throat boxes – like inflated Adam's apples – enable them to produce loud guttural howls that sound like a pig farm at feeding time. Howlers howl to advertise their presence to other howlers, thus avoiding adjacent troops and ensuring that the Park's resources are spread evenly amongst each group. The species feeds predominantly on leaves and unripe fruit, a low energy diet sparse in nutritive value. A howler has to eat lots of leaves to stay healthy. But the leaves are more predictably distributed than fruit, so in relative terms, howler monkeys need less space than squirrels. They also conserve energy by

Brown howler monkeys use their very loud voices to communicate their presence to each other

adopting a phlegmatic lifestyle in which up to two thirds of the daylight hours are spent resting, flaked out on branches, with early morning and late afternoon feeding bouts.

Eventually, even the squirrel monkeys become tired. Like all monkeys, with one exception, the South American owl monkey or douroucouli, squirrels are active by day or diurnal. "They end up grouping together in several trees where they huddle up in groups to stay warm," says Russ Mittermeier. "They're normally in bed by nightfall – about six o'clock. But they might keep moving if there's a full moon."

During the long, dark forest night, another assemblage of animals stirs and goes about its business. Accompanied by a cacophonous orchestration of unseen and untold millions of bugs, beetles and other invertebrates, some members of the ecological night shift search for prey that includes squirrel monkeys. The small primates may be easily surprised by large snakes like boa constrictors or small cats. Russ Mittermeier once observed a drama in the Amazon when a tayra, a big weasel-like creature, climbed into a sleeping tree after dark, created sufficient confusion and panic to scatter the squirrels, and ended up with a monkey meal.

In most places where primates live, the threat of attack from an occasional opportunist predator is far overshadowed by the threat from people. This is not the case in the Manuel Antonio.

"Grace has done a good job in habituating the monkeys to the presence of humans," said Russ as he and Julian marvelled at how close the squirrels came to them. "They see people along the roads and don't bother about them. It is different in the depths of the forests where they'd run away from us, although they're used to having Grace follow them."

Many tourists visit Manuel Antonio National Park each year. They come to use the beach and see the monkeys who have adapted well to the close proximity of people. Indeed, the non human primates are just as curious and inquisitive as the human ones.

"It's interesting," says Russ Mittermeier, "because it suggests that you can have a very endangered species cohabiting perfectly well with people. The only potential problems here are men with air rifles, boys with sling shots and stones, disease and capture for the pet trade. But Costa Ricans are pretty conscientious about their wildlife – in that sense they're more advanced than many other nations. The primatologists follow the monkeys closely and can monitor any harassment of them. Occasionally people take squirrels as pets but as long as the habitat is protected and there's no commercial trade for export to laboratories or whatever, I don't consider it a major problem – it's not going to result in the extinction of the species."

Managing man and monkey within Manuel Antonio National Park provides a series of benefits for all concerned. It would be impossible to keep humans out of the area, and any attempt to do so would result in resentment. "You'd wind up with poaching and illegal forest destruction," says Russ Mittermeier.

The project also fulfils the cornerstone objectives of Conservation International. Russ thinks that Manuel Antonio could serve as a model of good conservation management practice for other areas in the tropics. "We're going to see more and more of this type of park in the future," he says. "Justifying the existence of protected areas on the basis of

Primates are sometimes captured as pets by the local people. This child has a young spider monkey as a companion

the presence of one or two endangered species is not adequate for some tropical countries. You may also have to have a certain degree of human use of an area so that a part of it is used by people and the rest is left to wildlife. That provides an economic justification to the region. Local people benefit and the country as a whole benefits."

This is the way forward to the rainforests of the future. If such places are to survive, it will be because it is more profitable to keep them intact than to chop them down. So many rainforest plants harbour medicinal chemicals, oils, gums, resins, fibres and future foodstuffs that it would be dangerous folly to exacerbate our destruction of them and lose the world's greatest genetic storehouse forever.

Russ Mittermeier points out that, in the past, the economic value of a tropical forest centred around how much timber people could extract from it – a sort of mining operation. These days scientists are just beginning to investigate non timber forest products – strange fruits that can be eaten, made into soft drinks and ice cream; Brazil nuts; plants that yield substitutes for ivory and plastics; vegetation that produces industrial dyes and latexes. The list is endless and, as yet, barely tapped.

There is growing evidence that by allowing local people to influence the management of 'their' forests, by keying in to their boundless knowledge of forest products, and by adopting multiple use strategies that harvest a mix of products from particular rain forest ecosystems, the forest becomes far more profitable than clear felling trees ever was. It's a far cry from the Tarzan of old, but that is how Russ Mittermeier first embarked upon his lifelong battle to protect the planet.

"I was never really interested in anything else," he says. "As a kid I lived in the Bronx, New York City, and my mother would take me virtually every week to the American Museum of Natural History and the Bronx Zoo. She would read me books

Rainforest is a vast potential source of medicinal chemicals, gums, oils, resins, fibres and foodstuffs, and yet vast amounts of it are being irreparably destroyed every day

about Africa, and when I was eleven or twelve, I discovered the Tarzan books. I'd seen the movies but this series of wonderful books – some twenty four in all – really firmed up my interest in Africa in particular. As it turned out, I've ended up spending more time in Latin America.

"I was also a devoted herpetologist and collected snakes, salamanders, frogs and turtles all the time. There were several hundred tanks and basins in my downstairs playroom."

When Russ first visited the tropics, they more than exceeded his expectations. "It's amazing – it's so diverse, and what I really like about it is that it's so full of surprises. You can go into a temperate forest, which is also very attractive, but you have a pretty good idea of what you're going to see. In a tropical forest, you're never sure what you're going to stumble over."

There are hardships, though. Russ tells stories about the twenty four hour a day mosquitoes in the upper Amazon and the ever present risk of catching diseases like malaria and leishmaniasis. It takes several months of suffering before a western body becomes acclimatised to the tropical climate. And any self respecting primatologist has to keep in shape, particularly if he or she is chasing monkeys moving through the trees, or crawling along steep slopes to obtain a better view.

The greatest challenge is trying to keep up with uakari monkeys. These unusual primates have bald, red faces, long shaggy fur and are the only South American monkeys with very short tails. They are known locally as 'English monkeys' as they purportedly resemble a particular kind of Englishman with a liking for the gin bottle.

Uakaris live in swamp forests. For a good portion of the year their habitat is flooded – imagine a tropical forest two or three metres under water with the trees just growing out of it. The only way to follow these fast moving animals is by canoe with a local guide who knows the return route intimately. It is not an activity for the couch potato.

But discomfort aside, it is the very real chance of discovering a new species that really excites Russ Mittermeier. One of his favourite words is 'biodiversity'; the variety of life on Earth. Scientists have catalogued and described only about two per cent of global biodiversity. That means we know about 1.4 million species of animals, plants and other lifeforms. No one knows how many more species are out there waiting to be discovered. Estimates vary from thirty to one hundred million.

So the possibilities of exploring a rainforest and turning up something new are pretty high. Most of these new species will be small: probably insects. Some will become extinct without ever having been found by humans. All are in danger of being wiped out by our activities.

Occasionally, a new primate species is discovered. In 1990, a new species of lion tamarin, a miniature monkey related to marmosets, was discovered on a fluvial island near Sao Paulo in one of Brazil's most densely populated regions. "It's like finding a new monkey in the suburbs of LA," says Russ Mittermeier. And most exciting of all, on 12 October 1992, Mittermeier himself described a new species of marmoset which he discovered in the Central Brazilian Amazon; this discovery brings the total number of primate species for Brazil up to 68, by far the highest in the world.

This is a white uakari monkey. These monkeys are known locally as English monkeys, for their purported resemblance to a gin-drinking Englishman!

The yellow-tailed woolly monkey had not been seen or heard of for fifty years before this individual was rediscovered in Peru in 1974 by a team of scientists including Russell Mittermeier

Mittermeier was also involved in the 'rediscovery' of the yellow-tailed woolly monkey. First described by the famous German naturalist Alexander Von Humboldt in 1812, nothing more was heard of this animal, which occurs only in the cloud forests of the northern Peruvian Andes, until 1925 and 1926 when five specimens were collected for the British and American Museums of Natural History. A further fifty years elapsed before Mittermeier mounted an expedition to Peru and rediscovered the species in 1974. "Over the following ten years, we developed a conservation programme," he says. "A number of Peruvian scientists have been very effective in setting aside protected areas for the woolly monkeys and carrying out education and public awareness campaigns in the region. The yellow-tailed woolly monkey is the largest mammal that's entirely restricted to Peru. It also happens to be a very good flagship species for the highly threatened Peruvian cloud forests that are being cut down by immigrants from the poverty stricken Peruvian highlands."

The woolly monkey project and the Manuel Antonio National Park are success stories. In a world of environmental doom and gloom, they inspire Russ Mittermeier to carry on his work. "I think it's very important to be upbeat and optimistic," he says. "There are ways of achieving our goals, there are successes. We have to learn from these and try to replicate them in as many places as possible. Primates intrigue me; they're symbolic of biodiversity in general and excellent flagship species for the conservation of tropical forest ecosystems. These places are the ultimate expression of the complexity and magnificence of life on Earth. They're really nature's works of art, and to me they're worth conserving for this reason alone. I'm in this business for aesthetic, moral and spiritual reasons. That's why I'm so committed to primate conservation."

Russ is also a hard headed realist. As he believes, "by developing the appropriate strategies, by working with our colleagues in the tropical countries, we can turn today's conservation dreams into tomorrow's conservation realities."

CHAPTER TEN

THE WILDERNESS STARTS HERE

The British love the countryside. Every Sunday, many people drive away from the bustle of city life for some rural solace. We harbour secret thoughts that the urban sprawl is bereft of wildlife, and that true nature happens out there in the ancient woodlands, meadows and undulating fields of England's green and pleasant land. Some of us hope to recapture vague childhood memories of summers spent splashing in rock pools or picking blackberries. Perhaps our Sunday sojourns to bucolic pastures help us to find God in nature rather than in the half empty churches. We are possibly in love with the idea of 'the countryside' – an image of unspoilt beauty found everywhere from Constable paintings to TV commercials.

No wonder we are often disappointed when we get there. That is, if we get there. On any summer weekend, Britain's highways and byways are choc-a-bloc with tail to bumper car convoys, the motorways seize up, and the view from the vehicle window is an endless vista of flattened fields, oil-seed rape, littered laybys and industrial estates where mighty oaks once grew.

The countryside is changing. Indeed, it has always been changing. It was never just virgin wilderness nor monocultured food factory. In the words of Oliver Rackham, an eminent Cambridge University botanist, "the ordinary landscape of Britain has been made by both the natural world and by human activities, interacting with each other over many centuries."

When the interactions are one-sided and loaded in favour of short-term economic gains, the nature part of the relationship suffers. The loss of ancient meadows, woodlands and hedgerows is testimony to this, and has led many conservationists to consider the British countryside to be in crisis. In many respects this is true, but our abuse of nature must be balanced against the positive aspects of human interaction with wildlife. Sometimes our activities create new habitats and opportunities for animals and plants to flourish.

Jeremy Thomas and Ken Livingstone are two naturewatchers who are encouraging the development of such positive initiatives towards wildlife and wild places. Their approaches are different but complementary. One is an academic, the other a politician.

Dr Jeremy Thomas is one of Britain's leading authorities on butterflies. He is particularly interested in the wildlife potential of roadside verges and motorway margins. Ken Livingstone is the former leader of the defunct Greater London Council and a Member of Parliament for the Labour Party. Dubbed 'Red Ken' by the tabloid press, he was once the scourge of Margaret Thatcher's government and is widely feted

Naturewatcher Dr Jeremy Thomas, one of Britain's leading authorities on butterflies

as one of the most humorous raconteurs in the House of Commons. Livingstone is also an expert on newts and other amphibians. As an urban conservationist, he sees London and other cities as places teeming with wildlife potential. Ken's great cause is to reunite city people with nature via urban nature reserves, parks and garden ponds.

For *Nature Watch*, Julian Pettifer joined Jeremy Thomas on a butterfly safari in Dorset. Julian, a seasoned traveller, had presented *Nature Watch* from all kinds of habitats across the globe. But this assignment was different. He had never watched wildlife on an island in the middle of a busy thoroughfare before.

"Why on earth have you brought me to this haven of peace and tranquility?" asked Julian as a never ending stream of cars and lorries sped by. "Well, it's not my favourite piece of countryside either," replied Jeremy, "but despite this traffic and the urban area around us, this place is extremely rich in butterflies and wildlife in general." The two men began exploring. "Look at this ragwort," said Jeremy. "It's autumn now and there's no leaves left on it, but when I came here earlier in the year the ragworts were covered with cinnabar moths."

Jeremy has recorded nineteen butterfly species around the 'island' – a third of the British total. "There are not many nature reserves with more species than that," he says. Also staggering are the densities at which some of these species occur.

"This site has more meadow browns recorded per unit area than anywhere else in Europe I've come across," said Jeremy. "There's three adults per square metre which means about two hundred caterpillars in the same area. We've also found very large populations of marbled whites and quite decent numbers of common blues."

The roadside site in Dorset visited by Jeremy Thomas and Julian Pettifer for Nature Watch *had more meadow brown butterflies per unit area than any other site Jeremy knew of in Europe!*

Marbled white butterflies, one of the many species Jeremy Thomas found on a roadside verge in Dorset

Julian trod carefully. The area was pockmarked with holes. "It's like Swiss cheese," said Jeremy. "Probably made by short-tailed voles. I guess that in slightly wetter weather you'd be in danger of sinking straight into the soil."

Further searches turned up spiders, hoverflies and moles. "The moles create yet another variation to the habitat," said Jeremy. "Not only do they churn the soil allowing plants to seed in it, they also break the sandy surface which can really bake up in summer. Some of the ants like these hot, dry conditions and a few of the rarer species are found in these light soil patches. Grasshoppers often lay their eggs here as well."

Jeremy's interest in road verges grew out of a concern about the general decline of butterflies in the British countryside. He undertook surveys in many habitats to find out where the remaining species were, and only considered verges rather recently. "We ignored such areas for a long time," he said. "There was this idea that busy roads were hopeless for butterflies. Either they'd be killed by the traffic or they couldn't stand the fumes and noise. Gradually, as I drove past these places it made sense that they could be ideal breeding habitats for a good many species."

The majority of roadside verges have very few butterflies – the site in Dorset is quite exceptional. Jeremy looked at fourteen different roads and tried to say why some were so good and others were not. The main criteria for success in attracting butterflies are a profusion of food plants for caterpillars to eat and places for the animals to breed and lay their eggs. The amount of traffic going past has no influence at all on butterfly numbers. Some of the busiest roads have the most butterflies on their verges.

Despite the traffic, roadside verges can be a haven for wildlife such as butterflies provided the right food plants are present

Surprisingly few of the flying insects are killed by cars. In two studies on busy dual carriageways in Dorset, Jeremy painted up to a thousand butterflies a time with little coloured spots on their wings. Each animal was given a slightly different pattern and could be individually recognised. The roads were very little barrier to butterfly movement. The insects crisscrossed backwards and forwards quite freely and hardly any were struck directly by the cars that were speeding by at the rate of one every twenty to thirty seconds.

"What happened was that the air pressure created by the high velocity of the cars caused the butterfly to be swirled up in the air and dumped unceremoniously on one side or other of the verge," said Jeremy. "They didn't appear to like it very much but it didn't harm them. They'd pick themselves up after thirty seconds or so, fly along the verge and start laying eggs or feeding."

Dorset has more butterfly species than any other British county, partly because of the diverse geology and partly because it has one of the hottest local climates in the British Isles. The road island haven is obviously in the right locality and scores heavily on several butterfly friendly features.

"The bank that surrounds it creates an arena," said Jeremy. "It provides shelter and traps the sun. The temperature here is probably two or three degrees hotter than the open fields all around which is very good news for wildlife. There's very few grasses, a diversity of microhabitats and food plants, no fertiliser has been used and the native soil has been left. People spend enormous amounts of money importing rich, fertile top soil to many of these new roads. You end up with a brilliant greensward of one or two grass species, but relatively little wildlife. Thin, viable natural soil is cheaper and supports a much wider range of plants."

Roadside conservation happened by chance at this particular site. With research and management, Jeremy thought the island could be even better. "I'd do two or three things to improve it," he said. "First, the topography could be altered even more so we get a greater range of slopes, sheltered bits and even some north facing cooler areas. A few more shrubs would provide refuge and extra food, and I'd mow perhaps a tenth of the area nearest the road. Some butterflies prefer open habitats and we might attract rarer species such as grayling and silver studded blues."

Nature is a mosaic of species, habitats and situations affected to a greater or lesser extent by people. Most countries have relatively few, if any, large continuous areas of unspoilt wilderness. Habitats are often fragmented and not contiguous. In isolation they may appear unimportant for wildlife, but fit the pieces of the jigsaw together and the whole becomes greater than the sum of the parts.

Nowhere is this more true than for roadside verges which, in total, outstrip the countryside's nature reserves in area. "I've seen figures of half a million acres bandied around," said Jeremy Thomas. Most of these border motorways, and *Nature Watch* wanted to know if the occasional gains for wildlife from verges made up for the overall losses. It was time to hit the road.

Julian and Jeremy decided to investigate the M40, Britain's newest motorway that carves its path through some of the most beautiful countryside of the south Midlands.

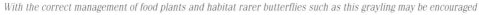

With the correct management of food plants and habitat rarer butterflies such as this grayling may be encouraged

They looked at a couple of sites to assess the environmental impact of the new route on wildlife. "We need to know whether this road has an adverse effect on wildlife," said Jeremy. "If it does, we must find out how to stop or reduce the damage, as well as discovering ways to attract flora and fauna here. After all, far from being the finale of our road building plans, the completion of the M40 is just the overture to a multi-billion pound new construction programme."

The first site visited was originally filmed by the *Nature Watch* team seven years earlier before the motorway was built. "This was a typical piece of land," said Jeremy. "Considerably better than the average piece of intensively farmed land but not a Site of Special Scientific Interest or anything like that. I'd describe it as a middling chunk of grassland and farmland – its true value lies in the meandering river and associated flood meadow that provided a feeding ground for ducks and waders."

Roughly one quarter – some one hundred hectares – of the flood meadow had disappeared altogether since the motorway arrived. A beautiful double meander was taken out of the river with the resultant loss of a quarter of a mile of river bank. Much of the river edge had been replaced with concrete, although a nature reserve was developed nearby to provide some compensation for the wildlife.

"The meadow is a major loss," said Jeremy. "Wetland flood meadows are a comparatively rare habitat in lowland Britain. No doubt the water birds have suffered. Curlews used to be a speciality of the site but they've disappeared. I think that resulted from disturbance during the motorway construction period rather than because of today's passing traffic. It's not necessarily a disaster. The curlews have probably just moved up the valley and are breeding elsewhere."

The river used to be home to a kingfisher. "It's not been seen this year," said Jeremy. "However, I understand that kingfishers come and go. They're not very faithful to individual sites and it's really too early to say if this one has left forever."

Away from the wetlands, an enormous new embankment of rough grassland had been created. Young trees were planted that would eventually close up and form thickets. "That's a plus," said Jeremy. "It will benefit the song birds when it grows. At the moment I should guess that the poor, knee high grass will be absolutely teeming with small mammals like voles, shrews and wood mice."

Larger mammals are a major problem. They have to be kept off the road from the safety point of view. Many motorways now have tunnels and bridges for badgers, deer and amphibians to pass through. Such devices do not always work. "I know for a fact that when this motorway was built, a great many badgers were killed in the early weeks after its opening."

For Jeremy's beloved butterflies, the site created extra habitat. "Water meadows are not very exciting for butterflies. Very few species breed there, but the drier bank will attract more. I do think though that if it had been seeded with a wild flower mix, the butterfly diversity could have been much richer."

According to Jeremy, we are moving in the right direction to obtain maximum wildlife benefit from motorway verges. Twenty years ago, the trend was to plant tulips and have billiard green lawns at the roadside. Now, native species are used and

The black hairstreak butterfly is a rare species doing extremely well on blackthorn which has been planted beside the M40 on the edge of Bernwood forest

Jeremy was encouraged to see willows, hawthorns and ash on the new bank. He awarded the site five marks out of ten and conceded that more could be done. Imaginative planting on the heavy clay soil would attract more species. Blackthorn, for example, supports a great variety of insects and provides a wealth of bird nesting sites. It may also entice brimstone butterflies to the verge.

Set against this are engineering considerations and money. The new road must be stable and cannot encroach too much upon the surrounding land. However, the Department of Transport and councils the length and breadth of Britain are nowadays much better at integrating wildlife needs with road planning policy. Much research is still required to determine rigorously the ecological effects of motorways on wildlife.

Research is Jeremy Thomas's profession. He took Julian to the place where he started his butterfly studies twenty years ago – a peaceful place on the Oxfordshire/Buckinghamshire border called Bernwood Forest. It was here that Jeremy did his PhD work on brown and black hairstreak butterflies.

Bernwood Forest is one of the remnants of a great ancient royal hunting forest of lowland Britain. It used to be massive – thousands of hectares of ancient broadleaved woodland on heavy clay soils. The high density of blackthorn attracted black hairstreak butterflies – it is the only plant they will eat. Long coppice cycles ensured that vast quantities of scrub were always available. Up to the 1950s, the forest remained intact. Now the broadleaved trees have been relegated to a fringe around a sea of black conifers.

The broadleaved edens have become even more important as refuges for the remaining butterflies. When Jeremy Thomas heard that the M40 was to bisect the woods, he was horrified. "This is one of the most important sites for butterflies in the whole of the British Isles," he says. "I am still appalled to see this great meandering motorway with all its noisy, polluting traffic coming through one of the most delightful spots of the south midlands."

The situation is not as bad as it might have been. After years of lobbying and public enquiries the original motorway plan was changed. At a cost of two million pounds, the route was altered, largely for the sake of the black hairstreak. The new road still clips the corner of the wood, but as a quid pro quo compensation, a piece of what was intensive farmland has been set aside for Jeremy to create what amounts to the black hairstreak's idea of heaven. "I have been given *carte blanche*, but it's a long term job," he says. "We've skimmed the top soil off and are landscaping the terrain. Then, we've planted tens of thousands of small shrubs in great scoops – predominantly blackthorn but a host of other species native to these woods like ash, oak, field maple and dog rose. It's almost a Hampton Court Maze and will take five to ten years to really mature."

On another occasion, Jeremy Thomas visited Julian Pettifer's garden. Julian said that he'd had more butterflies in his garden in 1991 than in any previous year he could remember.

"Yes, it's been good for things like small tortoiseshells," agreed Jeremy. "But having said that, you've done everything right to attract them into the garden."

Doing it right means having lots of nectar sources for butterflies to feed on. Large, old fashioned plants are best, particularly if they are growing in sunny, sheltered places. The relatively few species that are mobile enough to fly from the surrounding land to the garden will flit in and out to feed on the flowers and stock up energy for the winter.

If you *really* want a butterfly garden though, plant caterpillar food plants. Nettles are good, but most wildlife gardening books tell you to grow little clumps of nettles in a disused corner. The trouble is that butterflies are fussy about where they lay their eggs. They need lush green nettles growing in full sunshine.

Jeremy Thomas thinks that gardens are less important for butterflies than many people realise. "You get a false impression from the wonderful abundance of tortoiseshells, peacocks and commas," he says, "but the important places are those where butterflies can breed. Very few butterflies breed in gardens, whereas any semi-natural habitat with caterpillar food plants – like a motorway verge – is a better bet. Because of the size and sort of most gardens, individuals can contribute more to butterfly conservation by acting through organisations like Butterfly Conservation or the County Naturalist's Trusts."

Gardens may not be butterfly havens, but they are important sanctuaries for other forms of wildlife. Birds, bees, bugs, hedgehogs and foxes all use gardens for feeding, shelter and as green corridors through the urban jungle. A well managed garden becomes a personal nature reserve, attracting an abundance of species. Wild areas,

Butterflies are attracted to Julian Pettifer's garden as it provides good nectar sources in its large old-fashioned flowers. Gardens are important sanctuaries for all sorts of wildlife, from bees to foxes

organic vegetable plots and a pond are all good conservation accessories for the modern wildlife garden.

Ken Livingstone is particularly interested in garden ponds and their inhabitants. He is best known for his penchant for newts. Ken and Julian Pettifer teamed up for *Nature Watch* in order to search out Britain's rarest newt, the great crested. They discovered the amphibians in a disused swimming pool in the middle of Surrey. There they met Julia Wycherley, Surrey's County Recorder for Amphibians and Reptiles. Julia explained that an Amphibian and Reptile Recorder collates data about sites where amphibians and reptiles are found in a particular county. The information is added to a national database held at English Nature in Peterborough. It is a job after Ken Livingstone's own heart.

On this occasion the trio aimed to translocate the newts from the swimming pool to their former pond which had just been desilted, replanted and restored to its original depth.

The newts arrived at the swimming pool in mid February – it was the nearest body of water to their original breeding pond. Once in, the deep poolsides meant the hapless amphibians were stuck. Fortunately, great cresteds are the most aquatic British newt species and can sustain a long period in water.

"How do you catch them?" enquired Julian. "*You* don't," replied Ken. "They're protected by law so you have to have a licence in order to handle them – as I have just in case the local constabulary comes along. You'll be heavily fined if you touch one Julian, even though you're on TV!"

Ken Livingstone and Julian Pettifer on the trail of the great crested newt

The Ken Livingstone newt catching technique involves waiting until you see one coming up to breathe and then lunging underneath it with your hand. "They can easily stay under for five to ten minutes," said Ken. "The cooler it is, the less often they come up. Mind you, compared to some of the turtles, they're non starters. There are turtles who can breathe through the anus and stay down for an hour because their rectum's suffused with blood vessels. They just suck water in and extract the oxygen. Hang on, we've got a newt coming up."

Ken had captured a beautiful male great crested. "It's wonderful," he said. "He's in full breeding plumage as it were. There's a very pronounced crest along the back together with the black warty skin and dark spotted yellow underbelly. Look at those large testicles."

The newt was removed to the release pond. "This is ideal," said Julia, "because it's very deep – about two metres over there – and round the edge we've got some excellent float grass which is a marvellous newt egg laying medium." The new habitat would also allow the animals to leave the water after the breeding season. "They're great wanderers," said Julia, "they'll certainly roam further than the garden, perhaps between a half and one kilometre away from the pond." "And you can rely on them to clean up your slugs," added Ken.

Julian asked Ken if the time spent catching newts compared favourably with his activities in the House of Commons. "The company's more congenial here," quipped the MP, "they may be cold blooded but they don't shout at you all the time."

When Ken Livingstone is not working in Westminster, he can often be found beside his own garden pond. "Every place I've lived that had a garden, I built a pond in," he says. "When I left one house, the estate agents put 'pond designed by Ken Livingstone' in the property ad. I don't know if it increased the price or not.

"Then Tom Jackson, the old Post Office Union leader, bought a house with one of my ponds. He complained bitterly that I'd left the toads on purpose to keep him awake all night as part of a left-wing conspiracy."

Ken reckons that London has lost at least three quarters of its larger ponds over the last century. "That's why back garden ponds are now so important," he says. "Without them, a lot of aquatic life would be virtually extinct in London."

Building a pond, Livingstone style, means first putting down an underlay. "The problem in inner city areas is that the ground is full of thousands of years of human habitation – bits of glass, rocks and so on. The important thing is to have a layer so that the little stones don't eventually rub their way through to the pond liner and cause a leak. You can buy special underlay for ponds but people use all sorts of things – old carpets, newspaper, even sand."

Putting the liner in is less trouble than digging the hole, especially in London. "Go down a foot and it's solid London clay," says Ken. "It took me a couple of weeks just doing it on weekends and a morning or two depending on parliamentary time. I bunked off the madhouse, but digging was agony."

When the pond is ready to be filled, the liner is anchored down with large rocks at each corner. The water forces the pond into its correct shape and depth. Then the

Ken's pond is home to a fine collection of aquatic invertebrates and amphibians but fish are strictly out of bounds (they eat the amphibian eggs and tadpoles!)

liner can be trimmed with an ordinary pair of scissors. Once the water is in, the pond is left to settle on its own for a day or two. This removes the chlorine from the tap water before planting commences.

"You've got to have plants at the edge for cover," says Ken, "and then there's oxygenating plants that go right down to the bottom. Many of these will be covered in eggs of small animals. After a time, the pond goes completely green and many people panic at this point and pour in some dreadful chemical that kills everything. But the algae has to bloom, and if you put in daphnia or water fleas, they'll eat it. Then something will eat them. Part of the joy is watching the pond evolve into a balanced community."

Ken Livingstone's pond is open house to a myriad of aquatic invertebrates and amphibians. Two groups of animals are taboo: fish and cats. "People look at you as though you're demented if you exclude fish," says Ken. "But they're vacuum cleaners. They'll voraciously eat all your amphibian eggs and tadpoles – except for toads. Toad tadpoles taste terrible, apparently. Otherwise fish is off."

And cats? "They're a major problem," says Ken. "They sit at the pond edge and systematically hook out the amphibians. The best thing is to provide plant cover, like flag irises, around the perimeter so that frogs can hide. Don't forget also to scatter rotten log refuges around the garden."

As a boy, Ken Livingstone caught amphibians in his local park in Streatham. "Thirty years ago, there was a beautiful great fat toad that lived down this drain in the park.

It was always just out of reach of my skinny arm. Maybe it's still there. who knows? Toads can live for up to sixty years."

The young Livingstone had dreams of being the second David Attenborough and wrote to London Zoo for a job. They were not taking anyone on at the time. "I think it's just as well," says Ken. "I'm forty-six now and would probably be about to lose my livelihood."

He did maintain a large collection of reptiles and amphibians in his bedroom. "I had this great big monitor lizard that kept getting out. Everyone would lock themselves in their rooms until I caught it. My mother's only objection was if it became so enormous it might eat the dogs and have to go."

Ken's parents were not afraid of the collection. His mum liked the animals and his dad had spent twenty years in the merchant navy, so a few reptiles were not about to bother him. The only thing that got to them was the smell.

"All this stuff was going on at seventy-five or eighty degrees," says Ken. "If my alligator defecated at say nine o'clock in the morning, just after I'd gone to school, there was this great fishy turd bubbling away until everyone came home at five o'clock and the whole house smelled of alligator dropping." Nevertheless, Ken was developing his herpetological expertise and consolidating his interest in the natural world. His greatest captive coup was to be the first person to breed the Congolese frog in confinement. "It reproduced upside down," he remembers. "The only frog in the world that does it upside down. You had to have completely still water as they mated just below the surface film. If an aerator was going, they wouldn't breed."

Today, Ken fights for conservation in Westminster's corridors of power. He has been instrumental in setting up urban nature reserves like one five minutes walk from Kings Cross Station. A derelict area that the Greater London Council originally wanted as a lorry park is now packed with plants, ponds and a growing array of wildlife thanks to Ken. Thousands of school children see it every month.

Ken is aware of the global conservation problems that face the planet. He is well versed in green issues like global warming, rain forests, pollution and over-consumption by the so-called economic north. Many of these issues will be solved, if at all, by the actions of governments working cooperatively to maintain planetary balance. Ken Livingstone is dedicated to putting the environment on top of the political agenda.

He also realises that conservation needs public support to succeed, and believes that every individual can play a part in helping it to do so.

Ken walks round the garden every day before he goes into Parliament. He stares into his pond and unwinds. It helps him to find a release in nature away from the "insanity of western society".

We can all do this. Nature is all around us – even in the unlikeliest of places. You don't have to go to the rainforest or ocean, although it is a great privilege if you are able to do so. At home, you only need open your senses and heart to the environment. Then you will be a Naturewatcher too.

ACKNOWLEDGEMENTS

The authors and publisher would like to thank the following people for supplying the photographs in this book:

Harry Andrews (p. 49); David Breed (p. 6); Robin Brown (pp. 32, 64, 78, 84, 87, 88, 91); Jim Cronin, Monkey World (pp. 20, 21, 22); Steve Dawson (p. 124); Department of Conservation, New Zealand (p. 118); Mike Donoghue (pp. 112, 113, 115, 116, 119, 121, 123); Earthtrust Hawaii (p. 120); Raewyn Empson (p. 68); Jane Goodall Institute (pp. 10, 11, 13, 14, 16, 18); Itamar Grinberg/Jeff Rotman Photo (p. 38); Carl Jones (pp. 77, 80, 81, 83); Bryony Kinnear (pp. 85, 86, 90, 93, 94, 96, 99, 109, 111, 151, 152, 154); Hugo van Lawick (p.12); Don Merton (pp. 65, 66, 69, 70, 73, 74, 75); Russell Mittermeier (pp. 126, 127, 129, 130, 132, 133, 134, 136, 137, 139, 140); Roberta Rose (p. 45); Jeff Rotman Photo (pp. 36, 39, 41, 42, 43, 46); Margaret Shepard (p. 71); M. J. Skelton (p. 149); Helen Snyder (pp. 100, 104, 105); Noel Snyder (pp. 98, 102); Julian Thomas (pp. 142, 143, 144, 145, 146, 147); Romulus Whitaker (pp. 48, 50, 51, 53, 54, 55, 56, 58, 59, 60, 61, 62); Erik Zimen (pp. 24, 26, 27, 28, 30, 31, 33); Zoological Society of San Diego (pp. 106, 107, 108, 110).

INDEX